MW00345447

Great
Communication
equals # Great
Production

second
edition

Great Communication equals Great Production

equals

second edition

Cathy Jameson, Ph.D.

Disclaimer

The recommendations, advice, descriptions, and the methods in this book are presented solely for educational purposes. The author and publisher assume no liability whatsoever for any loss or damage that results from the use of any of the material in this book. Use of the material in this book is solely at the risk of the user.

Copyright 2002 by
PennWell Corporation
1421 South Sheridan Road
Tulsa, Oklahoma 74112

800-752-9764
sales@pennwell.com
www.pennwell-store.com
www.pennwell.com

Cover design, book design and illustrations by Brent Church

Library of Congress Cataloging-in-Publication Data

Jameson, Cathy.
    Great Communication = Great Production/Cathy Jameson.--2nd ed.
       p. cm.
    Includes bibliographical references and index.
    ISBN 0-87814-831-0
       1. Dentistry--Psychological aspects. 2. Communication in dentistry. 3. Dentist and patient. I. Title: Great communication equals great production. II. Title.

RK53 .J35 2001
617.6'023--dc21

                                                           20011058021

Printed in the United States of America

3   4   5   08 07 06

TABLE OF CONTENTS

LIST

OF FIGURES

Creations absolutely de novo are very rare,
if they occur at all; most novelties are only novel
combinations of old elements, and the degree of novelty
is thus a matter of interpretation.

— SARTON, 1936

*D*entistry is a rapidly changing and evolving industry. The clinical changes that have occurred over the past decade are immeasurable. The management changes have been equally evolutionary. Even though proven management principles remain foundational, the intricacies of those management skills develop and refine with the times.

Since the original writing and release of *Great Communication = Great Production*, I have completed my doctoral degree in psychology. In the long, eight-year process of completing my doctorate, I have learned more and stretched further than I believed possible. I have incorporated my learning into the consulting services of Jameson Management, Inc. It was important to me to make sure that the doctoral study and the resulting knowledge would be workable and meaningful.

The title of my dissertation is "Controlling Stress in the Dental Profession Through Effective Communication." During the research phase of the doctorate, I studied the following questions: If a dental team participated in a course of study on communication skills, would the following five hypotheses prove to be measurably significant?

- Would burnout and dropout be reduced?
- Would job satisfaction improve?
- Would personal relationships between team members improve and thus, the resulting teamwork?
- Would stress be reduced?
- Would production increase?

Even though the five hypotheses seem to make common sense, I had to undertake a scientific study that would either prove or disprove the theories. I did prove all five hypotheses showed statistically significant improvement following a course of communication skills training—written and taught by the author. My years in dentistry, both in my husband's practice and as a management consultant, led me to believe these premises were true. But I wanted to take those premises to the highest level of validation—scientific study. All of the management principles of Jameson Management, Inc. are based on the control of stress through effective communication, management, technological, and clinical skills. I believe the results of my doctoral study are significant to the industry and to the professionals themselves. The entire Jameson Management team remains committed to the principles of improving relationships with patients and team members, controlling stress, and increasing the financial rewards for work well done. I wanted to integrate the newly determined information into this revision of *Great Communication = Great Production.*

I am, and will always be, a teacher. I am proud to be an educator. I am as proud of my bachelor's degree in education as anything else I have ever accomplished.

Today I am doing what I love the most—teaching. I still teach in the classroom at several dental schools. But for the most part, my classroom is either in a conference room with a dental team, in a lecture hall with a group of dental professionals, or in my own learning center with consultants, colleagues, or special dental groups participating in our symposia. My classroom is different now. My students change every day. As a teacher, I am proud when my students—dental professionals throughout the world—learn the skills I am sharing, and when they incorporate those skills into their own lives.

People ask me almost every day of my life, "Where do you get all that energy?" The driving force of my professional life—the energy that drives me—is seeing a person go to a level they didn't even imagine possible. When any member of the dental team realizes their potential and talent as a result of our teaching, coaching, support, and encouragement, then I know I have served my purpose well. That's "where I get all that energy."

I didn't write THE BOOK on management. I have been both a student of great management experts and a student of experience, having learned from those who have gone before me and from life itself. I have been privileged to have people in my life who have taught, coached, supported, and encouraged me. This book is a combination of my own learning from respected mentors, from my academic studies and research, and from my personal experience in the dental profession.

Therefore, I cannot begin this book without giving thanks. There are more people to whom I am grateful than I can mention in this preface because I have learned from each and every person with whom I have interacted. From many, I have learned great lessons of life, not just lessons in academia. Those life lessons have been intertwined in all that I do. Thank you.

A special thanks to the following teachers, mentors, and coaches: Ron Reichert, Ph.D., educational training; Thomas Gordon, Ph.D. and Steve Emmons, communication skills training; Drs. James Riggs, Nancy Jones, Laurette Taylor, and Carla Johnson, doctoral and dissertation mentoring; Ken Anbender, Ph.D., life design, organizational development and well-being; Tom Hopkins, presentation and sales training; Ed Foreman and Zig Ziglar, goal setting and sales training; Karen Moawad and Dr. Burt Press, consulting training; and doctors/clients and their teams from around the world who have taught me every bit as much as I have taught them. I appreciate your support, and your belief in my teaching. Thank you for sharing yourselves, your practices, your joys, and concerns.

I am grateful to PennWell Books for the support of my study, my writing, and my passion for the now proven hypothesis that communicative ability and practice productivity are connected. It is with their enthusiastic support that the revision and launch of *Great Communication = Great Production* is taking place.

I have the world's best team. Their belief in our mission and their own passion for our work are immeasurable. Thanks to my entire consulting team. You go out every day to teach the Jameson Management, Inc. systems and strategies and bring success to dental practices throughout the country and the world. Thanks for your belief in what we teach and for your "road warrior" stamina! Thanks to my administrative and leadership team. You help me make things happen!! I could never keep up with my schedule and fulfill my writing, speaking, and consulting responsibilities without your encouragement and support. In addition, your faithful contact with our clients, network affiliates, corporate colleagues, and team members is flawless.

I am grateful for my loving and supportive family: my son and his wife, Brett and Amy Jameson, my daughter and her husband, Carrie and Jess Webber, my dad and hero, Derry Ebert, my mother-in-law and beloved friend, Dorothy Jameson, and my entire extended family. You are the best.

A special note of thanks and love for my partner, confidanté, best friend, and husband, Dr. John Jameson. You are the kindest person I have ever known. You continue to be my biggest fan and most patient friend. You listen when I need that more than anything else. You notice all the small things that make the big difference. You never let a day go by without telling me you are proud of me and that you love me. Thanks for "allowing me to become." Thanks for being a role model for me, our family, our teams, our community, and our profession. I ALWAYS know that I can count on you, and that you will be there. You're the best. I love you.

Finally, I give thanks to God for His strength, His wisdom, His guidance, and His support. Every day I pray that "If someone today needs to hear Your word, let me be a vehicle for You. If someone needs Your message, may I have the privilege of being Your messenger. I am nothing. You are everything. I pray I will be about Your work every day of my life and that my work will be pleasing in Your sight."

I know, through you, dear God, all things are possible. Thanks for being there. You are my greatest source of inspiration, answers, and energy.

I dedicate this book—and all of my work—to You.

Cathy Jameson

CHAPTER I
COMMUNICATION: THE BOTTOM LINE OF YOUR SUCCESS

Communication is the "bottom line" of success in business today. A person's willingness to become involved with a practice or organization, to say "yes" to the purchase of a product or service, and to remain active and loyal to that organization are a direct result of a team's ability to give and receive information. Thus, personal, professional, and financial success depends on communication.

This chapter will:

- set forth the goals of the publication
- describe results the reader can expect from studying the data
- "sell the benefits" of integrating excellent communication into the environment of a successful organization

CHAPTER 2
GOAL ACCOMPLISHMENT

Many similar threads run through the lives of successful people and successful businesses. The most common thread is that these achievers are committed goal writers. Without a clear understanding of the career path of individuals within an organization and of the organization itself, success becomes elusive. Goal setting—goal accomplishment—is the foundation for fulfillment in life and in business.

This chapter will:

- discuss the barriers to goal setting
- teach the "how tos" of goal accomplishment
- give the reader the "want to" to become a goal writer

CHAPTER 3
BECOMING A "PEOPLE PROFESSIONAL"

A professional cannot provide services or perform skills if clients/patients/customers are not confident that he/she is on their side. Building a level of trust and confidence is critical for professional relationships to develop. Only then can the professional have the opportunity to generate revenue.

This chapter will:

- teach the skills needed to draw clients to an organization
- define how the "people professional" focuses on service to achieve desired results
- illustrate the necessity for professionalism throughout the practice

CHAPTER 4
UNDERSTANDING PERSONALITY DIFFERENCES

There are four basic personality types. If the professional relates to all four personality types in exactly the same way, losing situations and relationships will result.

This chapter will:

- provide a solid understanding of the four individual personality differences
- suggest how to best relate to the different personalities
- give case studies and scripts for certain situations

CHAPTER 5
LISTEN YOUR WAY TO SUCCESS:
REFINING THE ART AND SCIENCE OF LISTENING

Listen your way to success? How can this "simple" tool be considered the number one management tool in business today? There is no greater asset to business success than being able to listen accurately to clients. This skill can make that cutting-edge difference between mediocrity and greatness.

This chapter will discuss:

- body language and tone of voice—90% of a message is received through body and vocal expressions
- passive listening—encouraging the client to share more information so wants and desires can be established
- active listening—listening to make sure that a client is being accurately heard—clarifying messages

Chapter 6
Getting Your Message Across in a Positive Way: Speaking Skills

Making sure that you are understood and accepted is no easy task. Just talking or lecturing will not get the results you want. Learn how to speak so others will listen. Open lines of communication rather than close them.

This chapter will:

- teach specific speaking skills
- define certain situations requiring special ways of sending a message
- provide scripts for a variety of situations—these scripts will be transferable to each unique organization

Chapter 7
Handling Difficult People and Difficult Situations

Relationships with clients are not always smooth and not always productive. Improperly handled disagreements or conflicts can dissolve professional relationships. Generating new clients is more expensive than stabilizing existing clients. It makes good business sense to nurture those relationships. When areas of concern develop that require negotiation, specific skills can be applied so acceptable solutions are developed.

This chapter will provide instruction on

- negotiation skills
- positive disagreement
- constructive confrontation
- either/or confrontation

CHAPTER 8
SPECIAL PEOPLE, SPECIAL NEEDS

Communication with children, their parents, and geriatric patients can make the appointments with these special people delightful. Both verbal and written communication can set the tone for a successful experience.

This chapter will:

- suggest methods of developing a wholesome environment
- suggest ways to prevent dysfunction
- detail step-by-step instructions for communicative success

CHAPTER 9—COMMUNICATION VIA TELEPHONE

The telephone may be the most important marketing tool you have in the practice. Relationships with patients can be made or broken on the telephone. As a marketing tool, the scheduling of appointments can be accomplished excellently on the telephone. It's important to be clear on the skills necessary to enhance the practice through "telephone relations."

This chapter will:

- teach specific skills of telephone etiquette that will further the professional image of the practice
- deliver instructions on how to achieve scheduling success via the telephone

- suggest ways to handle the irate caller and turn this difficult person into a congenial client

CHAPTER 10 — MAKING AN EFFECTIVE CASE PRESENTATION: GAINING TREATMENT ACCEPTANCE

In order to encourage a client/patient to say "yes" to specific recommendations, an effective presentation must be made. The steps involved in making a satisfactory presentation are specific. To achieve a desired result, a plan of action must be designed, practiced, and executed.

This chapter will teach individuals to do the following:

- build the relationship—establish trust and confidence
- establish the need (perceived/diagnosed)
- make the presentation/instill the desire to proceed
- ask for a commitment—close

CHAPTER 11 — HANDLING OBJECTIONS

Discover the benefits of identifying objections. Once objections are determined, learn the step-by-step process of overcoming the objections or barriers. Only then can you move ahead.

This chapter will:

- give guidelines for problem or objection identification
- deliver a step-by-step process for overcoming the objections
- provide scripts/verbal skills for practical use and study

CHAPTER 12 — FINANCIAL COMMUNICATION: THE FINAL CLOSE

Here may be your greatest barrier to treatment acceptance. Fear of cost is real. It's not to be avoided, but rather it is to be handled with professionalism and confidence.

This chapter will:

- outline financial options
- discuss healthcare financing systems
- offer communication skills to overcome the cost barrier

CHAPTER 13—NURTURE PERSONAL REFERRALS—YOUR BEST SOURCE OF NEW PATIENTS

The number one source of new clients/patients is personal referral. Thus, determining ways to maximize and encourage these referrals is vital to continual business/practice growth.

This chapter will suggest ways to:

- identify satisfied clients
- ask for referrals
  - verbally
  - written
- explain the necessary follow-up for referrals
- develop a program for the acquisition and recognition of referrals

CHAPTER 14
CONTROLLING STRESS IN THE DENTAL PROFESSION THROUGH EFFECTIVE COMMUNICATION: A DOCTORAL DISSERTATION

Stress, when out of control, leads to psychological and physiological debilitation. Illness, loss of productivity, and dysfunctional relationships can be the result of such stress. Businesses lose billions of dollars each year to stress-related illnesses. In today's business climate, controlling stress is critical to assure personal, professional, and financial success.

This chapter will:

- define stress in the workplace
- describe the negative and positive effects of stress
- provide instruction and resources for stress-controlling techniques

CHAPTER 15
...AND, IN CONCLUSION...

This closing chapter summarizes the benefits of learning to effectively communicate. It will provide encouragement and motivation to all members of the team to read, study, and apply the information that has been provided. There's no such thing as a "born communicator," but the skills can be learned.

COMMUNICATION:
THE BOTTOM LINE OF YOUR SUCCESS

*Believe that there is genuine magic in believing—and
magic there will be. For belief will supply the power that
will enable you to succeed in everything you undertake.
Back your belief with a resolute will, and you become
unconquerable—a master of men among men—yourself.*

— CLAUDE BRISTOL

My husband, Dr. John Jameson, is a practicing dentist. I had the
privilege of helping to put him through dental school, assisting
him during the beginning years of his practice, and then moving from the
clinical area to the business area to manage the practice. Through the
many years of being involved with the dental profession, I have become
keenly aware of the challenges that go on every day in a dental practice.

As a part of our management consulting firm, Jameson Management,
Inc., consultants and our network colleagues now have been in more than
1,700 dental practices teaching the management principles and strategies
that I have developed. I have lectured in 10 countries to date, and we have
consulted in every state in the U.S. Our experience is vast. We have been in
every type of situation from the very beginning practice to the very mature
practice; solo doctor practice to multiple doctor practice; every specialty,

KEYPOINT:

Be in the business of taking care of people: your patients, your team members, and yourself. If you don't take good care of yourself, you won't be physically, psychologically, or financially healthy enough to stay in business. If you aren't in business, no one wins, and you certainly won't be able to take care of patients any longer. Give yourself permission to take care of yourself, as well as others.

including numerous medical specialties. We have consulted from Manhattan, New York to San Jose, California, and hundreds of large and small communities in between. Even though it is certainly true that every doctor, team, and practice is unique, I am sure we have coached a practice that is very similar to yours.

The first step in our consultation process is to conduct a comprehensive evaluation of the practice. We carefully listen to the goals and aspirations of the doctor or doctors, their spouses, and their team members, analyze all their systems, and design a strategic plan of action that will make it possible for each doctor to have the practice of his/her dreams. Why should anyone proceed through life or through a career and not realize the ideal? That just doesn't have to happen. I cannot imagine anything more painful than getting to the end of a career or to the end of a lifetime only to look back with regret saying, "I wish I had…." I hope each and every one of you can look back on your career and your life and say, "I am glad that I did…."

That is what we do at Jameson Management, Inc. We make it possible—through effective business, personnel, communicative, technological, and clinical skill training—for you to have the practice of your dreams. Care enough about yourself to accept nothing less.

You are healthcare professionals, and your number one commitment is to your patient's health and well-being. However, you are also running a business. Combining the two is not without challenge—but it can be done. I would like you to consider taking your commitment to care one step further.

Throughout our years in dentistry, John and I have found that my background in education, psychology, and communication has been an asset to our own dental practice and to the practices of our many clients. We have built the business aspects of those practices and our management consulting company on a solid foundation of educative, communicative, and psychological expertise.

Our success has been based on a commitment to educate patients about the value and benefits of dental care and to communicate those values effectively. These communication skills make it possible for dental teams to perform the excellent clinical skills that bring health and/or beauty to patients.

In addition, when working closely together, team members will naturally have difficult situations arise. Without effective communication, relationships cannot survive and thrive. I think you will agree with me when I say there is no one on any dental team that is more important than anyone else. Each person on the team has the power to make or break a relationship with a patient. Each person has what business calls "a moment of truth," and in that moment, a person's decision to proceed with the dental care or not can be helped or hindered.

Another dental consultant once asked me why I felt that I needed a Ph.D. in psychology to be a dental management consultant. After I recuperated from my shock at the question, I simply asked two questions: "When was the last time you were chairside with a patient?" and "When was the last time you tried to help a dental team get along with each other?" Psychology is the science of human behavior. I would say we deal with human behavior every day in our practices, wouldn't you?

I can teach you scheduling, financing, insurance management, hygiene retention, and all of the other management systems that make up the life of a dental practice. I can teach you until I am "blue in the face." But if the team isn't functioning cohesively and productively; if patients are not accepting treatment because of poor communication on the part of any team member; or if there is not a system of cooperative management in place, nothing else matters. Your chances of realizing your ideal practice will be compromised. Life is too short and too precious for that kind of compromise. You work too hard not to fulfill your purpose, to satisfy your every dream, to be everything you want to be.

PURPOSE

Dental professionals, working as a team, have, as their purpose, the care of the oral cavity—a vital organ of the body affecting the entire body. At the same time, the dental professional is responsible for educating people about the need for excellent care of the oral cavity, with the goal being optimum health and well being.

The oral cavity is an organ of the body that is not only a physically functioning system of the body affecting all other systems, but it is also an organ of the body uniquely reflecting attitude and emotion. It is considered an intimate zone of one's body—protected and shared cautiously. Through the mouth, words of conversation expressing thought and emotion are transmitted. The oral cavity is one's vehicle for communication, both verbally and physically. Thus, the dental professional is commissioned to care for one of the human being's most psychologically expressive avenues.

You, as a dental professional, must determine and care for a person's physical needs through careful diagnosis and treatment and be able to educate a person as to the value of recommended treatment or therapy for the oral cavity. You must be able to communicate effectively all of the above and be able to deal with a person's psychological needs as they relate to problems or issues involving this organ.

In order to satisfy all of these requirements, the dental team needs to be well skilled in the art and science of effective communication. Without effective communication skills, none of the above-mentioned challenges can be fully met and fully satisfied. If these challenges are not satisfied, the practice will suffer from low productivity, and the professionals may suffer from poor self-esteem. In addition, stress can get out of control when conflicts between team members and patients develop as a result of frustration and anxiety.

FOUR AREAS OF "NEED DEVELOPMENT" FOR THE DENTAL PRACTICE

Four strong areas of need have emerged through my years of research and work within the dental profession. These prominent needs are as follows:

Stress management. Dentistry has the number one suicide rate among professionals. Dentistry ranks as one of the leaders in drug abuse, alcoholism, divorce, and professional drop out.

What leads to this extreme stress? What can be done to relieve, or control, this stress? Can effective communication help to alleviate some of this uncontrolled stress? Can effective communicative skill lead to resolution of problems—problems that might otherwise be causing stress?

Staff fulfillment. The turnover in dentistry among auxiliary is an issue of concern for the industry and for individuals. Turnover of auxiliary is costly, both psychologically and financially. Dr. Burt Press has said that every time a doctor loses a key team player, this turnover costs the doctor the equivalent of one year of that person's salary.

What leads to dissatisfaction among dental auxiliary? Can effective communication systems be developed that will serve as vehicles for personal growth and personal satisfaction between and among dental professionals with the end result being less turnover?

Practice management skills. Dentistry is a healthcare profession, with the service of people as its main purpose. However, dentistry is also a business, and unless the doctor and his/her team are able to manage their practice as a smooth running and *profitable* business, they will not be able to remain in business. Thus, they will not be able to serve people. Every management system within the practice must be established and administered with clear objectives and monitored results.

One of the management systems within the practice is the system of case presentation/treatment acceptance. A barrier to optimum success and fulfillment within the dental industry seems to be the inability to gain case acceptance. Most dentists have more dentistry sitting in the charts than they have ever done in their practicing years. This undone dentistry can lead to financial stress and professional dissatisfaction. Therefore, one of the most important practice management systems within the practice is the system of case presentation and treatment acceptance. This seems to be the system that gets the least attention.

Communication skills are not taught in dental school, and there are very few courses offered or dental books written on the subject of communication skills as they apply to case presentation.

I would suggest that thorough diagnosis, complete treatment planning, and excellent case presentations are the fulcrum of your practice and everything else springboards from that. It doesn't matter how well you finance, schedule, manage hygiene retention, or anything else if a person does not say "yes" to your recommendations.

My husband, John says this: "When I took case presentation from being an aside in my practice to being the main focus, I took the lid off my practice."

Communication skills. I am thoroughly convinced that communication is the bottom line of success within a dental practice today. A person's/patient's willingness to:

- become involved with a practice or organization
- say "yes" to the purchase of a product or service
- remain active and loyal to that practice
- refer others to that practice

is a direct result of the team's ability to give and receive information clearly and accurately. Thus, personal, professional, and financial success depends upon effective communication. Indeed, *Great Communication does equal Great Production.*

GREAT COMMUNICATION?
WHAT ARE THE BENEFITS?

If you are going to undertake a study of communication skills; if you are going to work toward the improvement of these skills; if you are going to implement these skills into your life, you must see the benefit. In his book, *GMP: The Greatest Management Principle In The World*, Dr. Michael LeBoeuf says that all behavior is driven by "what's in this for me?" There is much truth in that statement. I want to present you with some possible bottom line benefits. This study of communication will benefit you in the following ways:

- Excellent management skills and systems will be enhanced by improved communication. Performance of team members will improve, and those team members will be more productive
- Fulfillment and satisfaction within the workplace will result, and you will kindle or rekindle your love for your profession
- Quality relationships among and between team members will develop when effective communication and effective problem-solving skills are learned and used. You will experience less burnout and dropout of team members caused by unresolved conflict
- Stress will be controlled.
- Relationships with patients will be enhanced, and this will lead to increased production and revenues for the practice. People will accept your treatment recommendations, stay with you (no more falling through the cracks), and will refer others to you

WHAT IS COMMUNICATION?

Communication is not the simple transmission of data. Webster defines communication as "the act of making known; intercourse by speech, correspondence, messages, etc. The imparting of information. To reveal; to convey." According to Thomas Gordon, Ph.D. and the author of *Leader Effectiveness Training*, "Communication involves the sending and receiving of both the content and the intention of a message. If stress is to be controlled between parties, accuracy and clarity in both the sending and receiving of the message must be evident." Rudolph F. Verderber says in his book, *Communicate!*: "Simply stimulating ideas and feelings will not always result in effective communication. One person may communicate with another in such a way that the communication has a different meaning for each person. Effective communication is a transactional process of sharing meaning." John D. Rockefeller once said that 85% of success is related to people skills, and that 15% of success is related to the technical skills. People skills and the ability to communicate effectively go hand in hand.

Think of your relationships with your patients. Is the success of your relationships centered around your excellent dentistry or around the level of care with which you handle the patient? Most of you probably answered the question by saying something like, "The patient seems to notice everything except the dentistry. They want and expect the treatment to be excellent, but everything else seems to have a stronger impact." Without question, the clinical dentistry must be superb. However, most of you would probably agree that patients make decisions based on just about everything else besides the dentistry.

Doesn't it make sense to be excellent at both? Can you combine your excellent clinical skills and your commitment to comprehensive, quality dentistry with a coinciding commitment to excellent communication? Will both you and the patient benefit as a result of this dual commitment? I think so.

How you communicate with patients, combined with outstanding personal service, will affect whether or not a person will complete the six-step cycle desirable with every patient. The six-step cycle is:

- They come to you
- Accept treatment
- Schedule and keep their appointments
- Pay for the services—gladly
- Stay actively involved with your practice through hygiene
- Refer others to you

However, even though most people will agree that communication is the bottom line of success, very few people undertake an active study of the skills. Communication is often taken for granted. You might be saying, "Some people are just born communicators." No, they aren't. Communication is a skill. Because it is a skill, or a set of skills, it can be studied and learned.

Communication is a process—a two-way process in which each of the parties within a situation is responsible for the success of the communication.

How many times do you hear what a person is saying but totally misinterpret the meaning? And vice versa, how many times do you send a message only to have it misunderstood? Did you not send a clear message? Did you not have the ability to get your point across? Or did the receiver of the message get too hung up in his/her own feelings to give you the attention necessary for an accurate interpretation? All of these are relevant questions when learning how to communicate more effectively.

That's why you have selected this book. You know that the success of your relationships, the success of your practice, and the success of your career balance on your ability to communicate. You are making a conscious decision to get better at these skills. You are on a continuous path of improvement, and I congratulate you for that. I have taught communication skills for 25 years, and yet I continue to study and make an effort to improve. The day I quit trying to learn more or to improve my skills is, certainly, the day I need to stop teaching. I have so much to learn and so far to go in improving my own communication skills. Learning will never stop. It is an ongoing path of life—a healthy path.

APPENDIX A, included in this book, is a study guide to go along with this book. It is structured as group lesson plans so you can study the book together. Together, as a team, you can set a goal to improve both the communication and the productivity of your practice. Follow the teaching within this book. Practice the skills. Incorporate these new skills into your every day, and you will see incredible growth. Study hard. Practice with intention. Enjoy the process.

KEYPOINT:

Communication is dynamic, not static. Communication is a mutual transaction between parties. Effective communication means that when a person sends or receives information, a clear or accurate understanding of the message results.

CHAPTER 2

GOAL ACCOMPLISHMENT

*When you have achievable goals for every day written
down, every day becomes an exciting contest with yourself.
You get up in the morning with a plan for making that day
contribute the most that it possibly can to getting what you
want from life.*

— TOM HOPKINS

I cannot start a consultation, lecture, or this book without stating what
I consider to be one of the major foundations for success—goal
accomplishment. Many similar threads run through the lives of
successful people and through successful businesses. One of those
common threads seems to be that these achievers have written goals—a
plan for their own success.

In order to master any new skill, including a communicative skill, you
have to, first of all, get your mind focused on that successful mastery. St.
Mark said: "All things are possible to him that believeth." Napoleon Hill
continues that thought process by saying, "Whatsoever a man can conceive
and believe, so shall he achieve." And Earl Nightengale simply says, "You
become what you think about."

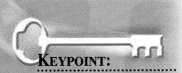

KEYPOINT:

Set goals related to this ideal practice, and maximize one of your greatest assets: a focused mind.

KEYPOINT:

A goal is defined by Webster as "the end result toward which effort is directed."

While once considered a theory, data today show there is truth in the above statements. Your actions will follow the dominant thoughts of your mind. Therefore, be careful what you think about! If you believe something can become a reality, then you have taken a critical step in making that happen.

In order to develop your ideal practice, to become an excellent communicator, and to create and maintain your dental dream team, you must first have a clear focus, a clear vision in your mind of what that looks like to you. Get that picture comprehensibly diagramed in your mind. What does that look like? What does that mean to you? What is your ideal practice? What is excellent communication? Where would you like to improve? What is your dream team? In other words, write a clear vision of what your ideal practice looks like, and then be about the business of making that happen (Fig. 2-1a and Fig. 2-1b).

Without the energy, the focus, and the intention of your mind, you dilute your effectiveness. Work on focusing your mind on the things that can be accomplished rather than on the things that might go wrong, but probably won't. If you decide something cannot happen, I promise you, it can't. Carefully focus on constructive thought processes. Get your mind set—confidence will lead you on.

A goal gives you a clear vision of the result of specific actions or behaviors. Goal definition helps to clarify the reason behind each of your day-to-day activities. You will see more clearly that each and every day, and the activities of those days, are stepping-stones to the goals you have set. This process is motivational. It gets you up in the morning, keeps you going throughout the day, and sometimes into the night! Goals become that guiding light that pulls you through the thick and thin of it all.

My definition of a great dental team is as follows: "A great team is a group of leaders working cohesively toward a common set of goals."

Jameson management inc.

Vision Worksheet (part 1)

Page 1

"Defining your vision is like going on an adventure. It's a difficult assignment and consequently a challenge. There are unknown aspects and therefore a high risk. And there is potential for great reward."

—*Jack Linkletter*
CEO, Linkletter Enterprises

1. Type of treatment being provided:

Doctor:

Hygiene:

2. My ideal patient visit: From beginning to end, what is a patient's experience like with us at each and every appointment?

3. Our team: What are they like—attitude and aptitude? What are their responsibilities?

Business Administrator:

Assistants:

Hygienists:

Laboratory:

4. Our facility: Does it reflect your "ideal"? If yes, how? If not, what would you change? What would make it the "ideal" facility?

5. My equipment and technology: Am I up to date? Is the entire team fully trained? Are we using the technology to its maximum capability? Is it being used to enhance our patient care? Is it paying for itself?

6. Number of days worked per month:

7. Hours per week:

8. Number of vacation weeks per year:

9. Amount of production/collection:

Fig. 2-1a: Jameson Vision Worksheet, part 1

Jameson management inc.

Vision Worksheet (part 2)

Page 2

10. Take-home salary (gross):

_____

11. Reputation in community:

_____
_____
_____
_____

Now Ask Yourself...

How do I make this happen? _____
_____
_____

What's getting in my way? _____
_____
_____

What will I do to overcome my own barriers/
obstacles? _____
_____
_____

Whom do I need in my life to help me?
_____
_____

Whom do I need as a resource person or
company? _____
_____

_____
_____

What's getting in the way of me inviting
these resources into my life? _____
_____
_____

Why? _____
_____
_____

What do I need to overcome my own
resistance? _____
_____
_____

What will be the benefits of having
resources/coaches/helpers in my life?
_____
_____

Will I do this? _____
_____

When? _____
_____
_____

Fig. 2-1b: Jameson Vision Worksheet, part 2

WHAT IS A GOAL?

A goal does not become a goal until it is written down. Unwritten, a goal is only a dream or a wish. It is okay to dream and to wish. Do so! But take the dreams that mean the most to you and work at turning those dreams into realities.

Many people have a vague idea of what they want to achieve in life, but very few spend the time and energy to plan for successful achievement of specific goals.

HARVARD UNIVERSITY

Harvard University and Dr. David McClelland have spent a great deal of research time and money on the study of motivation. In studying motivation, they wanted to find what major attributes characterize successful people.

They found that one of the key characteristics of successful, highly motivated people is that these people are goal-oriented. In fact, Harvard found that 80% of the productivity in the U.S. is accomplished by 20% of the population. In analyzing this productive 20%, the researchers discovered that this group was, in fact, goal-oriented, but only 3% of the group wrote down their goals.

Expanded study of these people uncovered the fact that the 3% who were goal writers managed to increase their own productivity by a minimum of 10%, and they increased their personal incomes by approximately 100% within a year from the time they began writing their goals.

YALE UNIVERSITY

Yale University performed a similar study. They surveyed a class of graduating seniors, asking if the individuals wrote down their goals. Again, 3% said "yes." (3%! Remember—different university, different researchers, and different researchees! Same result!)

The university tracked this group of graduates for 20 years. At the end of that 20-year period, they found that the 3% of the graduates who had written their goals, and who had continued to do so, had

KEYPOINT:

Give up the things in your life that are not working and focus on the things that are working.

accomplished more than the other 97% of the graduates put together (in measurable entities, including financial success!).

Our Own Personal Study

On a personal note, John and I began writing our goals at a time in our lives when we needed to grow personally and professionally. We had been very successful in our dental practice and in other businesses, but the oil crisis hit Oklahoma, and what we had been doing wasn't working anymore. So we thought, "Why keep doing things the same way?"

We had the privilege of hearing a tremendous motivational speaker and management expert, Mr. Ed Foreman of Dallas, Texas. Mr. Foreman was addressing a group of dental professionals at the Dallas Midwinter Meeting (now, the Southwest Dental Conference), and was encouraging us to become more effective managers of our lives and of our businesses. He encouraged us to "get control of your lives" and start doing that by writing down goals.

We decided the whole concept made too much sense not to do it! Besides, it couldn't hurt. We began to study the art and science of goal setting and goal accomplishment. I wanted to know why only 3% of the population writes goals and commits to the process if such tremendous results can be achieved. I personally wanted to know about goal accomplishment because we didn't just want a 10% growth in our practice; we needed to grow by that much—minimally!

Within a year from the time we began writing our own goals, we had increased the productivity of our practice by 35.5%, and we had in fact increased our personal income by about 100%. In one of our state's most difficult economic times, we had begun a journey of continuous growth and prosperity—a journey to personal fulfillment and happiness that continues even now.

Today, we still write down our goals and will do so forever. We have learned that getting ourselves and our team focused on a common set of goals and working together toward the accomplishment of those goals provides the guidance, motivation, and focus needed for continuous progress to occur.

Goal setting was and is the foundation of our success process. For the past decade and a half, I have studied everything I could find on goal writing, goal setting, and goal accomplishment. We have incorporated this process into our professional and personal lives. The process works better than I had ever expected. The key is getting the mind in the right place and believing that each and every worthwhile goal set and processed can be accomplished.

REASONS PEOPLE DO NOT WRITE THEIR GOALS

You may be saying to yourself, "If this goal-setting business is so great, then why don't more people do it? If the success rate of the 3% is so tangible, why don't more people take this step?"

Good question! There are several reasons why people choose not to write their goals:

- Fear of failure
- Low feeling of self-worth, lack of confidence, low self-esteem
- Don't know how
- Don't know their goals
- See no reason

Let's look at each of these potential negatives. If you face a negative before the fact, you have a chance to turn that potential negative into a positive. That's what I hope to do—turn any negatives, or reasons why you might not write goals, into positives.

FEAR OF FAILURE

You may ask, how in the world does fear of failure relate to goal setting? Many people hesitate to write a goal down in black and white, because then, if the goal is not accomplished, failure will be seen as the result. "If I write it down and don't get it done, then I will be viewed as a failure." People fear failure because they see it as a defeat, as a negative. "If I'm not quite sure of myself anyway, then to fail at goal setting will just solidify my perception that I'm not so great!" There is a commitment made when a person writes down a goal. That commitment is to oneself, and that commitment may be the most difficult one of all.

The dental professional is often caught in the trap of believing that he/she must be perfect. The environment in which the dentist performs is extremely small, and there is no margin for error. The dentist believes that he/she must meet the needs of all people, relate exceptionally well to all

KEYPOINT:

Thomas Gordon, Ph.D. says: "Courage is not the absence of fear, but the willingness to act in spite of fear."

people, be a top notch leader of the dental team, be the total provider for the team and for family, and must not show any emotions that might be misconstrued as negative.

Robert Eliot, M.D., in his comprehensive study of stress management has found that "Perfectionism is expectation that never meets reality, and it is fueled by the fear of failure. It is comprised of guilt, defensiveness and the fear of ridicule. Clues to this behavior are the words, should and have to. Perfectionists believe and practice the adage, 'If you want something done right, do it yourself.' Unable to delegate even the most minor tasks, they become angry with themselves or others whenever any detail can't be done just right."

This perfectionist misconception leads to incredible stress within the dental professional— usually, but not always, self-induced stress. To write down goals, to put these down on paper, to expose them to one's conscious self or to others is

THOMAS EDISON: GREAT ATTITUDE!

Long ago, Thomas Edison, considered one of the greatest inventors in history, was working on the acquisition of a light source. He tried and "failed" in many of his attempts. In fact, he performed more than 10,000 experiments on this light source that did not work! One day a friend asked Mr. Edison if he hadn't become discouraged after failing more than 10,000 times in his efforts. Mr. Edison replied, "Failed 10,000 times? I didn't fail 10,000 times, I simply learned 10,000 ways NOT to make a light bulb!"

What a way to look at a situation! He saw the positive value of the learning rather than the negative effects of perceived failure. It's not what happens to you that makes the difference. It's what you learn from the event.

If you set a goal, and you find that the strategies you have set forth to accomplish that goal don't work for you, don't quit! Learn from your experience.

viewed as a possible opening for others to see the humanism, reality, and imperfection that might result if these goals are not obtained. So, it is safer to leave goals, desires, or dreams tucked away in the safety of the subconscious self.

The only way to overcome a fear is to face that fear head on. When we face that fear, deal with it, and survive, we take great strides in overcoming the fear. Address fear by doing exactly what you fear the most. Once you discover that you can do something and survive, the task will be more comfortable for you the next time. Facing a fear takes a great deal of courage.

The fact that you have faced something you have previously feared is a success within itself. Not ever facing an issue or a task you fear takes away from your very being. This stifles your journey toward self-fulfillment.

In evaluating the fear of failure as it relates to goal accomplishment, let me propose a different view of the matter. Instead of looking at not accomplishing a written goal as a failure, look at it as "new learning." You have just learned that the plan you have been following does not work for the accomplishment of a particular goal. You now know you need to step back, take a new look, develop another plan, and come at the accomplishment of your goal in another way.

The only failure that relates to goal setting is this—if you learn and understand the benefits of goal setting and never even try, then I think you have failed to give yourself the opportunity to be all that you can be. In addition, you have failed to give yourself one of life's greatest gifts—the power of a positively focused mind, the opportunity to maximize your talent, and the fulfillment of your life's purpose and inner-most dreams.

LOW SELF ESTEEM

Some of you are not overwhelmed by the issue of fear of failure, but you have decided for yourself that you are not worthy of success or the achievement of a particular set of goals. You may not have a fear of failure, but rather, a fear of success. You have told yourself so many times that "I can't," "I wouldn't be able to," "I couldn't possibly," or "I'm not worthy" that your subconscious mind has come to believe you.

The subconscious mind doesn't know the difference between reality and non-reality. So, if your subconscious mind constantly receives messages about your lack of self worth, it begins to believe this is true. Efforts to feed your mind positive input about yourself, your abilities, and your desires or

goals are essential for growth. You can begin to overcome a feeling of low self-worth by feeding positive thoughts and nutritional information into your mind.

DON'T KNOW HOW

Most people have never had a course in goal setting, goal writing, and goal accomplishment. If goal writing is so valuable for success in life, shouldn't this course of study be offered in school, perhaps a required course? But then, success in life is not required, is it? We choose to be successful, and we choose to be unsuccessful!

Since you are reading this book, you have made a statement about your desire to get in control of your dental practice, and you have made a statement that you want to be successful.

One of the main reasons that people do not write their goals is that they don't know how. However, by the end of this chapter, you will have had a thorough lesson on goal setting. Therefore, not knowing how to write goals will no longer be a legitimate excuse!

You may not have all the information you want or need on goal writing at the end of this chapter, so I encourage you to seek other books on the subject and discover all you can about this key to success.

Turn your dreams into reality. When you begin writing your goals, allow your imagination to be set free. Put your every dream down on paper for the purpose of visualizing and analyzing each one. If you don't think you have any dreams, think again. Reach down deep into your gut, pull out any passions you may possess, and write them down. You may have been indoctrinated to put away your dreams, not to "bother with such trivia." Most people have been taught to do just that, and unfortunately, have been taught very well! Now

I'm recommending that you "pop the top" and let those dreams bubble out of your inner self.

Remember—a dream does not become a goal until it is written down. You may be asking, "Why do I have to write it down? I know what I want!" Writing the goal down serves several purposes:

- It then becomes something you can visualize. It becomes tangible.
- Written down, it becomes something you can refer to for evaluation and any necessary modifications.
- Evaluating your path toward the reaching of the goal lends a sense of gratification and positive reinforcement for work well done.

Educators and psychologists have told us for decades that the key to solidifying behavior is to positively reinforce that behavior. When you take a step forward on your journey to success, when you take a step toward the accomplishment of a goal, pat yourself on the back for that forward step. This reinforces your efforts.

In working on your self-esteem, which you must constantly do, this reinforcement delivers a sense of satisfaction that you can do something and that your efforts have been fruitful. You see the results of your efforts and are encouraged to continue to put forth effort. In other words, you stay motivated.

DON'T KNOW THEIR GOALS

If you don't know what your goals are, consider this method of discovery. There are three distinct kinds of goals. These are separate, yet interrelated, areas of your life:

- Personal, family, and spiritual goals
- Business and career goals
- Self improvement goals

The three areas are so interrelated that it is difficult to separate them. Your degree of wellness (your physical, emotional, spiritual, and mental fortitude) definitely affects your work, which in turn, affects how you feel about yourself, which affects your family life, and so on. There is a connection between the three areas.

Zig Ziglar teaches that in each of these three areas of goal definition, one must generate thoughts on who and what you want to BE, what it is you want to DO, and what you want or desire to HAVE. Once you have set your imagination free; once you have reached down deep into your gut to pull out your inner most feelings, thoughts, and desires; once you have written down what it is you want to be, do, and have in each of the three areas, it is then time to begin putting a process of accomplishment into motion. According to Mr. Ziglar, "You've got to Be before you can Do, and Do before you can Have!"

Use Figure 2-2—Jameson Goal Worksheet: Goals—the Dream List—as a springboard for the initial discovery phase of your goal-setting efforts. Note that all three types of goals are indicated here. Write what you want to be, do, and have in each of these areas. If you are a person who does not, at this time, know what your goals are, this may help you get started.

Prioritize your goals. Make a supreme effort to keep your goals and your life in balance. Let nothing get in the way of maintaining that prioritized balance. Prioritize your goals so that you don't spend your time doing things that are not of uppermost significance to your days and to your life. Some people spend all of their time on things that don't make the big difference and never get to the significant tasks of their days and their lives.

You may be saying, "Yeah, but, that's not easy. I have so many things pulling at me that it's difficult to prioritize! Everything is a priority." I can appreciate this thought process and concern. In the busy and demanding times in which we live, there are indeed so many pulls that organizing your priorities may seem impossible. Let me give you some suggestions.

Define each goal as a high, medium, or low priority goal. Consider the following:

- High priority—MUST be done
- Medium priority—SHOULD be done
- Low priority—WOULD BE NICE if it were done

At the end of every workday, write down six things that you need to do the next day. Then prioritize these six things using the high, medium, and low priority rating system. If you have two things that must be done the next day, list them as A-1 and A-2, etc. You'll have to think this through sometimes, because placing one prioritized task over another may seem impossible—but you can do it.

GOALS
THE DREAM LIST

Jameson management inc.

PERSONAL/FAMILY

Children	**Car**
Spouse	**Vacation**
Home	**Money**

BUSINESS/CAREER   SELF IMPROVEMENT

BUSINESS/CAREER	SELF IMPROVEMENT
Salary	**Physical**
Benefits	
Career Development	**Mental**
Equipment	
Financial security	**Spiritual**

Fig. 2-2: Jameson Goal Worksheet: Goals—The Dream List

Once you have your list prioritized, read it and put it in a place where you can retrieve it easily the next day. As you begin the next day, reread the list. Focus on your number one prioritized task. Work on it until you get it done or get to your predetermined stopping place; mark it off, and go on to the next task. No matter how many times you get interrupted, once you can refocus, go back to the original task.

KEYPOINT:

"In the span of a lifetime, which of these things is the most important?"

Using this proven time-management strategy, you will get more done in less time than you can imagine. Plus, by organizing your mind, you will rest better and/or will enjoy your non-work time more because your mind will not be constantly working at getting organized. Follow this principle for your short term and daily goal setting. But, follow the same principle with your long-term goals. Again, don't get to the end of your life and "wish you had done….." but rather, get to the end of your life and "be glad that you did….."

Here is a question I ask myself when trying to decide between two prioritized goals or tasks: "In the span of a lifetime, which of these things is the most important?"

That question seems to always bring me to a definite and clear decision. When I am torn between two opportunities or between two responsibilities and have to choose between them, this is the question I ask myself. Give it a try. Clarity seems to follow.

SEE NO REASON

As I said at the outset of this chapter, I am a committed goal writer, but I haven't always been one. I used to write my New Year's resolutions faithfully, but I never really followed a process of goal accomplishment with commitment and enthusiasm—now I do.

It was during the most challenging of John's practicing years that we began writing goals—individually and as a team. I shared with you the impact that Ed Foreman had on us, and the impact goal writing had on the health of John's practice. We have never swayed from that commitment once we really saw the concrete results that came from getting our heads in the right place, adjusting our attitudes, believing all things are possible, and incorporating a process of goal accomplishment into both our personal and professional lives.

Stress is definitely controlled when there is a clear plan of action outlined, and progress toward the completion of that plan can be tracked and evaluated. So many doctors and team members have told me they sense a great deal of frustration by either not knowing the status of a certain project or system within their practice or by having a lot of great ideas discussed during a team meeting, only to have no concrete results following the discussion.

By following the process I am about to teach you, you will see those two very legitimate frustrations vanish. Let me "sell you on the benefits" of goal setting. Goal setting and the goal accomplishment process will provide the following benefits:

- One of the best time management principles ever developed
- Proven motivator of people in the work force today
- Increase the productivity of the individual members of the team, thus improving team effectiveness
- Empowerment of team members as they participate in the development of the goals and action plans. Being a part of the decision-making process is another proven motivator
- Offsets procrastination
- Results are obtained much more quickly
- Production of the practice will increase by a minimum of 10%
- Personal incomes can increase by as much as 100%

Now ask yourself this question—"Is it worth it?" I hope you said "yes." If you see a reason to follow this process, you will make the time to do it. It just doesn't take that long! If you think it is taking too much time, go back and reread the above list. Then, ask yourself the question again: "Is it worth it?"

HERE'S HOW TO DO IT

1. Write the goal

Writing the goal down is the first step to accomplishing the goal, not the final step! Just as visualizing the end result of a crown preparation does not make the preparation happen, simply writing the goal down on paper does not make it happen. Just as you have a specific process for that crown preparation, you must have a specific process for goal accomplishment. Each process does have a step one, and in the process of goal accomplishment, that first step is to write it down. That's like writing a contract with yourself. Decide what it is you want, and begin the process by writing it down.

Make sure that your goals are SMART. Dr. Ken Blanchard, author of the One Minute Manager series, says that your goals need to be SMART:

S — Specific

M— Motivational

A — Attainable

R — Relevant

T — Trackable

LET'S LOOK

AT THESE REQUIREMENTS IN DETAIL.

S—Specific. In writing your goals, be very specific. The mind needs a very clear picture of what it is that you want to accomplish. So be specific, not general. Be generous in the visual details that you write down and that you play and replay in your mind.

For example: A goal that says, "I want to be a better communicator" is a good goal, but it's not specific enough. Your mind will not be able to focus clearly enough on this to visualize it as a reality. In addition, designing a plan of action to accomplish this goal would be challenging. It's simply not specific enough.

Rather, the goal might be something like, "I will study the skill of listening so I can determine my patient's 'perceived needs'—their emotional hot buttons. I will do so by learning to ask questions and listen accurately."

M—Motivational. There needs to be a reward attached to the accomplishment of a goal. Again, referring to Dr. Michael LeBoeuf, he says, "That which is rewarded is repeated." That is what Dr. LeBoeuf calls the *GMP: The Greatest Management Principle in the World*. A reward doesn't have to mean money. All people are motivated by different things. Money is a motivator, no doubt. However, according to the studies of Dr. Lawrence Lindahl, appreciation is a stronger motivator for employees than money. In fact, being appreciated was the strongest of all rated motivators while money was fifth. Interestingly, employers thought that money was the strongest motivator and appreciation was eighth!

Also remember, when your team is working toward a goal that they have written and designed together, it is valuable to celebrate the small victories along the way (Fig. 2-3). All too often we see disappointment and frustration raising its vicious head when a goal is being worked toward, but has not been completed. People allow themselves to dwell in a world of disappointment if the end results don't happen overnight or in a miraculous fashion.

KEYPOINT:

Don't forget to celebrate the small victories along the way.

Rather than do yourself this horrific disservice, let me encourage you to notice even the smallest of steps taken toward the accomplishment of the goal. When you take that one tiny step, you get so much closer to the desired end-result. The human being responds more effectively to positive reinforcement than to negative.

For example: If you are early in your study of communication skills, you won't say and do everything perfectly right off the bat. (In fact, you won't ever do everything perfectly!) But, acknowledge that you are trying and that your goal is to improve relationships, improve case acceptance, or be a better listener (or whatever). If someone you are working with doesn't respond positively to this acknowledgement, then someone has a problem, but it isn't you!

So, team of leaders, pat each other on the back, and pat yourself on the back each time you take a constructive step forward. Keep the end result clearly focused in your mind, but don't forget to celebrate the small victories along the way. This may be the greatest of all motivators.

A—Attainable. I encourage you to continually set your goals a notch higher each time you reach one. Be on a continuous path of improvement. However, don't set your goals so high that you set yourself up for disappointment.

Celebrate the Victories!
(Even the small ones!)

It is very important that the team take the time and effort to reach around and pat itself on the back. If you wait for others to recognize your work, you may wait for a very long time. Too often, others are quick to criticize, but slow to praise. So, when you've accomplished a goal, improved your processes, installed a new system, or put a new service into effect, celebrate the event! Congratulate yourselves, throw your own party, give out gifts or simply bring in a pizza!

Many team members work behind the scenes. They aren't on the front lines getting immediate feedback from patients. They don't have the visibility and may not get "kudos." They keep the ship afloat by making sure that bills are paid on time, payroll is completed and checks go out, information is distributed accurately and in a timely fashion, etc. As the saying goes, no one ever calls to say "thanks for getting my check to me on time." It's just expected.

Think of examples of this in your own practice. How can you express appreciation for one another more effectively?

Have your own celebrations when certain milestones are accomplished. But remember to express gratitude for the every day activities that make it possible for you to perform excellently. Also, remember to be a role model, an example. If you pat others on the back, you set the tone for them to do the same thing.

Ways We Will Celebrate Our Victories:

1.

2.

3.

4.

Fig. 2-3: Jameson Small Victories Exercise.

For example: If right now your percentage of treatment acceptance is 50%, and you wish to improve this through better communication and case presentations, then you might set an initial goal of working toward a 75% case acceptance. Once you begin to consistently achieve that, then you could go up another notch, etc.

R—Relevant. Your goals must be relevant to your own personal value system.

They must be congruent with the who that you are. The goals of your practice—the short-term and long-term goals, the small and large goals—must be aligned with the mission or purpose that you are serving. In fact, your goals are the stepping-stones leading you to the ultimate fulfillment of your mission.

Here is a benchmark question that will assist you in your decision-making process. Ask yourself, "If we set and accomplish this goal, will it help us to reach our ultimate mission/purpose?"

If the answer to that question is "yes," then you are on the right path. If the answer is no, then you may need to rethink your goal.

If your goals are not in alignment with your values or ultimate mission, you won't put forth the necessary energy for their accomplishment. The results of your goal accomplishment process will be in direct proportion to the amount of energy you put into them. Energy output and goal accomplishment are equitable.

T—Trackable. Again, writing down your goals is a must for goal accomplishment to become a doable system in your practice and in your life. Writing down the goals gives your mind the visual image necessary to see it as if it were already done. Remember—your actions will immediately go to work to bring to pass the major

KEYPOINT:

Your goals must be relevant to your own personal value system.

KEYPOINT:

"If we set and accomplish this goal will it help us to reach our ultimate mission/purpose?"

thought processes of your mind—"You become what you think about."

My friend, Dr. T. Warren Center says, "A goal is a dream that is better defined."

I totally agree with his statement. With this process, you have the opportunity to bring your dreams into reality. The writing down and tracking of the goals also lets you analyze your progress— are you on course or not? If not, you have a chance to make any necessary adjustments and get back on course. If you are on course and are making progress, you can celebrate that small (or large) victory. Don't forget to pat yourself or your team members on the back for taking the steps toward, or for the actual accomplishment of a goal.

For example: If you and your team have set a goal and a member of the team has completed his/her part of your action plan, give him/her a statement of appreciation, either one-on-one or at a team meeting. Giving a team member a sincere and well-deserved compliment in front of the other team members is very reinforcing. He/she will feel good about the work and the accomplishment. More importantly, he/she will be motivated to stay on that productive path.

For example: "Heather, thanks for stepping in and helping me with those instruments yesterday. I was so backed up that I was stressed to the max! I really appreciate your help."

Tracking your progress keeps you aware of your progress and the efforts of each person who is working on the goal. These progress reports give you a chance to:

- stay on track
- not lose sight of a valuable goal
- note progress and be able to recognize the work well done

MAKE SURE THAT YOUR GOALS ARE SMART!

2. Design the plan of action

Determine the objectives or strategies necessary for the accomplishment of the goal. What must you do to reach this goal? How will you do it? Why is each part of the plan essential to the whole?

Don't forget to answer the "why" question. If someone on your team is to be motivated to carry out a part of the plan, he/she needs to clearly understand why the carrying out of each responsibility is necessary. After all, that is really what teamwork is all about—being able to count on one another to carry out related tasks. In other words, if one person's ability to get something done is dependent upon another person finishing their task, there must be trust that each person will fulfill their responsibility. Otherwise, progress is stopped.

During this step of goal accomplishment, identify resources you will need. What people do you need to access? What books do you need to read? What courses do you need to attend? What tapes do you need to listen to? Do you need financial assistance? Do you need instruments? Technology? etc. Who will coach you?

Also, identify barriers that might get in the way of the accomplishment of the goal. Then figure out how you are going to overcome those barriers.

If a barrier exists that might prevent you from accomplishing your goal, then carefully identify that barrier so you can begin to chip away at it. Work at eliminating barriers so there are no walls in the way of your success.

KEYPOINT:

A problem is only a problem until it becomes defined. Once it becomes defined, it becomes manageable.

Brainstorming is appropriate here. Brainstorming means that all ideas are shared in a very accepting environment. In other words, you may not like someone else's idea, but you are not going to rip it to shreds. Acceptance of another person's view does not mean you agree. It simply means you respect the other person enough to hear his/her view or idea.

Once all ideas have been brainstormed and written down, go back and discuss each one—the pros and the cons of each. Come to a consensus agreement as to which idea or ideas you believe will best help you accomplish the goal.

3. ASSIGN RESPONSIBILITIES TO THE APPROPRIATE PERSON OR PERSONS

Define who will perform or carry out each task, each action step. If a person on the team has been actively involved with defining, writing, and planning the team goals, that person will respond with enthusiasm when given the responsibility to perform related tasks.

If a person on your team knows what to do, how to do it, and why to do it, he/she will usually perform excellently, and things will get done in an expedient manner.

4. TIME ACTIVATE EACH STEP OF THE PLAN

Define the time frame in which each aspect of your plan is to be completed. It is essential that time frames be specifically outlined and recorded. This will allow people to hold themselves accountable, and the doctor or manager can hold each person accountable, as well. This critical step of the goal accomplishment process offsets that dreaded disease of procrastination! After you have designed the specific plan of action, put it into action! So many practices fall short right there! They know what they want, they design a great plan, but they never expend the energies necessary to put the plan into action. Follow Nike's recommendation: "Just Do It!"

5. EVALUATION

On a specific, pre-determined, regular basis, analyze how things are going. Are you on or off course? Do you need to adjust your plan? What have you learned from the proposed plan of action?

If you find that things aren't working so well, then step back and ask a few questions: "Do we really want to achieve this goal? Are we truly motivated to get this done?" and if the answer to those questions is "yes," then ask, "What's working?" Keep doing those things. Also ask, "What's not working?" Change your action plan right then and there. A Chinese proverb defines insanity as, "Doing the same thing and expecting a different result."

I follow the above outlined process. I write down the six things I need to do the next day, and prioritize my lists so that my daily goals are, more than likely, going to be accomplished. For my longer-term goals, I follow the five-step process of goal accomplishment, carry my goals with me, and read them no less than once per week. There is no way I could keep up with my progress or the progress of the people with whom I work if I didn't have a careful plan of action, time frames, and faithful evaluation.

KEYPOINT:

The definition of insanity: "Doing the same thing and expecting a different result."

—*Chinese Proverb*

Of all the things I can teach you for your personal and professional fulfillment, this may be the most significant. Certainly as we begin this study of improved communication and improved production, setting goals and following a specific process of goal accomplishment are foundational.

MY FATHER, THE ARCHITECT

My father is a brilliant architect whose artistic talents and masterful knowledge of science and engineering have become a statement of who he is. He is one of those extraordinary people who leaves an indelible mark on history and on the lives of those people he touches with his work and his love of it.

I often think of his profession of architecture and building when I am teaching the skills of goal setting. The end result of one of his designs is a beautiful, functional structure serving those for whom the edifice was constructed. When the building is completed, a celebration usually takes place to christen the facility and to share appropriate accolades to the builders, the engineers, and to the architect.

The process of getting to this point is long and tedious. The process begins many months, perhaps years, before the celebration of the completion takes place. The process begins with an idea—a goal. Then, very detailed, specific plans are drawn and written, describing to the nth degree what must happen before the structure is completed, and the goal is accomplished.

The goal is set, the plan is designed, and the plan is then put into action. Work begins. Specific objectives and strategies are assigned to specific people. Everyone knows his/her responsibilities and is held accountable for the completion of those tasks. A time limit is set for the accomplishment of each task so that the goal of a finished building is met in timely manner. Evaluation is an everyday process. How did this fit in with that? How will one portion of the building process prepare the way for the next phase? Are they on schedule? Are they heading in the right direction, or do they need to make adjustments in the original plan? And, so on.

And then the building is completed. The goal is accomplished. Celebration is in order. And it is good.

But I have learned a great lesson of life from this great architect—the joy does not come from the end result as much as it comes from the process of doing. The true joy and ultimate reward is the process of creating—the planning, building, growing, and the journey on the way to the celebration.

Here's the process:

- Write the goal
- Design the plan of action
- Assign responsibilities to the appropriate person or persons
- Time activate every part of the plan
- Evaluate
- Celebrate

A GIFT YOU GIVE TO YOURSELF

It has been said that many people spend more time planning their vacation than they spend planning their life, and I believe this is true for the most part. We must know where it is we want to go if we are to ever get there! So many people spend an entire lifetime wandering around, and then looking back and wondering where life went or wishing they had done something differently! I don't know about you, but I want to look back on my life and say "I'm glad I did ....!"

Design a plan for your life, and then be about the business of detailing that plan. Become an architect for the structure of your life. Start with a 20-year forecast, and work backwards—ten years, five years, one year, monthly, weekly, daily. A whole bunch of well-managed days make for great weeks, which lead into satisfactory months, excellent years, and a goal-oriented, goal-satisfied lifetime.

Setting goals for a lifetime seems somewhat overwhelming, I know. But don't think that your goals cannot or will not change. Keeping your goals written down keeps you on track and allows you to make those very necessary changes that evolve as you evolve. Set long-term and short-term goals. A clearly-defined set of short-term goals will be necessary for the accomplishment of your long-term goals.

Figure 2-4—Jameson Goal Worksheet:Goals and Objectives—shows a format for goal writing that we use in our client's practices on a regular basis. This is a great form to use during your team meetings or strategic planning sessions. This form will guide you during the development of your projects and goals. Some offices like to keep these posted so everyone knows the status of the goal. Or, copy the goal sheet and make sure that everyone involved with the project has a copy. Then, keep a three-ring binder of the goals so you can evaluate the progress during your team meetings.

TEAM GOALS

In the early part of each year, have each team person write two kinds of goals—individual professional and career goals (what that person wants to accomplish in his/her position in the practice this year), then, write a suggested list of team goals (what he/she would like to see the team accomplish this year); (Fig. 2.5)

One of the characteristics of an outstanding leader—and remember, each of you is a leader—is to be aware of the goals of the members of the team and to help your teammates accomplish their own goals. In an environment where people are able to fulfill their professional goals, people will be more likely to stay, be more productive, be more motivated, and will feel empowered and valued. As for the practice, when the energies and talents of the team members are focused, those energies become convergent rather than divergent, and the practice cannot help but thrive.

Take the team goals that everyone has written, and combine those to create a set of agreed-upon team goals. Follow the five-step process for

Jameson management inc.

GOALS AND OBJECTIVES

GOAL:

Objectives/Strategies	Responsible Person	Time Frame	Evaluation
#1			
#2			
#3			
#4			
#5			
#6			
#7			

© Jameson Management, Inc.

Fig. 2-4: Jameson Goal Worksheet: Goals and Objectives

accomplishing those goals, and watch out! You will have ignited a powerful energy force.

There isn't a thing you can't get done when you follow this system and focus your talents like a laser beam. As you are evaluating your goals, you will be amazed and gratified at how much you have accomplished.

Jameson management inc.

Name: _____

THIS YEAR'S GOALS

Personal Career Goals: What I want to accomplish in my position in the practice this year. _____

_____

_____

_____

_____

_____

_____

_____

_____

Team Goals: What I would like to see the team accomplish this year.

_____

_____

_____

_____

_____

_____

_____

_____

Fig. 2-5: Jameson This Year's Goals Record

If you want all members of your team to have a sense of co-ownership in the practice and to feel challenged by trusted responsibility, then make goal accomplishment a part of your practice.

You are, indeed, in control of your destiny. You are responsible for your success or your failure. Choose to succeed. When you decide to be successful, you will be. Make the commitment to control your life. Start with goal accomplishment.

In Summary

The first step to success is deciding to be successful. The next step is to gain control of your life. You begin that process when you write your goals! I hope you will work on any fear of failure that may have prevented you from writing your goals prior to this reading. I hope you will see yourself as a beautiful, worthy human being with wonderful opportunities available to you in your practice of dentistry. I hope you now see a reason to write your goals, and that you have a better understanding of how to go about that writing. But most of all, I hope you will start NOW to begin your journey to success and happiness.

Write the word "procrastinate" on a piece of paper, light a match and burn the paper! Procrastination never helped anyone accomplish goals! Start now!

BECOMING
A "PEOPLE PROFESSIONAL"

*Render more and better service than is expected of you if
you wish to achieve success. People who render the
greatest service also uncover the greatest opportunities.*

— NAPOLEON HILL

A professional cannot provide services or perform skills if clients, customers, and patients are not confident, and if they do not have a steadfast level of trust. Building a relationship of trust and confidence is perhaps the most critical step toward a person's acceptance of you and the treatment you are providing. This may take more time than any of the other parts of case presentation, but without it, you will never encourage a person to say "yes" to your recommendations.

Becoming an excellent provider of customer service, which is what being a "people professional" is all about, makes the difference. Remember a patient might not know that you spent extra time and put extra effort into those margins. But, they will know how they were treated on the telephone, how they were greeted, how comfortable they felt in your chair, how well you listened to their concerns, how respected they felt in your office, how you filed their insurance, how you handled their financial situation, etc.—everything but the dentistry.

When my son graduated from medical school, the Surgeon General of the U.S. at that time, Dr. David Satcher, gave the keynote address. He looked out at the 150 graduates and said, "Young graduates—doctors—you have had the finest medical and clinical training available today. Now, make a commitment to focusing on the skills that may make the greatest of all differences for your patients: the skills of communication. And the communication skill that may be the most important is the skill of listening." He was encouraging these care-providers to focus on their people skills and combine excellence in clinical expertise with excellence in communicative expertise.

Your clinical expertise must be above reproach. The dentistry has to be excellent. Most people base their decision on whether or not to proceed with treatment, whether or not to stay with you over time, and whether or not they will refer others to you based on the dentistry and a whole lot more. That's where the people skills come in. That's where being a people professional and an effective communicator makes the difference!

What can you do in the dental environment to encourage and nurture that valuable, yet elusive quality of trust? What can you do to enhance your people skills so that you become a people professional? The following are 10 proven strategies.

10 Ways to Become a People Professional

1. Define your ultimate mission or your purpose

Write a statement of mission that becomes the foundation of all you offer. Then, commit to accepting no less of yourself or the members of your team. In your mission statement, define the type of care you will be offering and how that care will be focused on the service of your patients. As Stephen Covey says in his book, *Principle-Centered Leadership,* "A personal mission statement based on correct principles becomes a personal constitution, the basis for making major life-directing decisions, the basis for making decisions in the midst of the circumstances and emotions that affect our lives. It empowers individuals with timeless strength in the midst of change."

Make sure that you offer only the best possible care—without compromise. Let your patients see this commitment to quality shine through in everything you do: your facility, your team members, your written correspondence, your treatment, and all follow-up. Offer only the best. Make a statement to the patient, that says: *"We think you are special and way above average. Therefore, our goal is to provide you with special care that is way above average. You are worth the very best."*

2. Make sure that you are providing the type of care that patients want and expect

Find out how you are doing by asking questions or by asking patients to complete a performance survey (Fig. 3-1). Do not become defensive to the responses. Use this vital information to improve your performance. Make sure that you are serving the needs of your patient base.

Ken Blanchard, Ph.D. in his book, *Raving Fans*, states that finding out what your clients think about you is imperative. He says that when people say everything was "just fine," you better look further. Not finding out what may have gone amiss is dangerous to the health of your organization. It is healthy to find out where things can be improved so you can do even better.

Dr. Blanchard also states that having satisfied customers in today's competitive world is not good enough. Rather, you need to create "raving fans"—people who receive everything they expect and a little more every time they have an encounter with your office.

Determining what your patients want can also be determined by very carefully analyzing their behavior. Are they expressing pleasure with their experience in your practice? Are they saying "yes" to treatment? Are they staying actively involved in your hygiene department? Are they willing to refer others to you?

Dr. Blanchard states that there are three D's involved with creating "raving fans:"

D—Decide.   Decide what kind of services you are going to provide. Be very clear about your vision

D—Discover.   Discover what your clients/patients want and what they need in order to be exceptionally pleased with your service

D—Deliver.   Deliver what is expected—and a little bit more—every time

PATIENT SURVEYS OR QUESTIONNAIRES

Successful corporations do surveys and questionnaires on a regular basis so that they change with the times and with the changes in client desires. The companies that listen to their clients and respond rather than react are usually one step ahead of the competition.

Gathering information from your patients puts you in a position to respond to the wants and needs of your patients. You can find out what they like about you so that you can do more of that. You can find out what they don't like so that you can consider change. You can also determine what services might be of interest to your patients so that you can begin to offer those services.

The survey should be short and easy to complete. The questionnaire can be structured for yes/no answers, or you could structure the survey in an evaluative style, such as, "Rate the following from poor to excellent." Then list 10–20 questions for the rating. Close the survey with an open-ended question, such as "if you could change one thing about our practice, what would you change?" or "What would you like us to offer that we are not presently offering?" or "If you were going to recommend us to a friend or family member, what would you say is our best quality?"

You can either send the surveys out to your patient family, or you can ask them to complete the survey while they are in the office. If you mail the surveys, make some kind of special offer if they return it to your office. Be aware that if people are going to offer constructive criticism of your practice that they may not want to sign the survey. That's okay.

As you are asking people to complete the survey, explain that you are trying to improve your services and want their input so that you can be sure you take excellent care of them. Presented in this manner, most people will respond positively and will complete the survey for you.

Patient surveys are a fabulous way to find the strengths and weaknesses of your practice. What a powerful way to evaluate your position and to set goals for improvement!

Fig. 3-1: Patient Surveys or Questionnaires

3. APPLY ETIQUETTE IN ALL AREAS AND IN ALL RELATIONSHIPS IN THE PRACTICE

Study and practice excellent telephone etiquette (refer to Chapter 9). The person's first impression of the practice usually occurs during that initial telephone call. Surveys have shown that 7 out of 10 patients make a decision as to whether or not they will schedule an appointment by the way they are treated during the first call.

My dentist husband, John, believes the telephone is the most important marketing tool he has in the office. I think he is right. Make sure that everyone is answering the telephone in the same manner every time. Enthusiasm, warmth, and concern need to be evident in each phone conversation.

Careful messages must be taken in a message book that has carbon copies. Post messages so the responsible party can promptly return telephone calls from patients. You always want patients to know that their call is important, and getting in touch with them to answer questions is not only okay, it is desired. Make them feel as special as they really are!

Stand and greet each patient as they come into the practice. Greet them by name as you welcome them into your dental home. Sincerely inquire about their well-being and about their family. Know something personal about all of your patients. Record this personal information in your computer or on a special form in your charts. Become aware of this personal information during your morning meeting. Upon arrival, make them feel at home by mentioning or inquiring about this personal information. Make sure that what you mention is positive. You will want to start the appointment on a positive note. Treatment will proceed much better with a positive mindset in place.

Introduce yourselves to all new patients. No matter what your position in the practice, introduce yourself and let the patient know your role in their treatment scenario.

For example: "Mrs. Jones, I'm Cathy. I'm Dr. Jameson's clinical assistant, and I will be working with you today. We're glad that you've chosen our practice for your dental home, and we will do our best to make your time with us pleasant. You may come with me now." Be positive, encouraging, straightforward, and informative.

Doctors, introduce yourselves or make sure that the team member who is with you during your first exposure to the patient introduces you. I recommend a handshake. Why? You will soon be entering this person's mouth. Remember—the oral cavity is an intimate zone of the body. Therefore, it is critical that you establish a physical contact before providing your oral health evaluation. The handshake is proper etiquette. But, it becomes even more essential as you understand the body language of dental care.

4. Provide a full range of services—professionally, financially, and emotionally

As a people professional, you are concerned with the total person. You understand the connection between oral health and total wellness. You also understand how a person's self image and self-confidence are enhanced or degraded by the smile. A person's comfort with their smile affects their sense of well-being.

Because of the connection of the oral cavity and the smile to the entire person, you need to offer a full range of services or be able to make those services available through trusted referrals. In addition, present a full range of financial services so the financial needs of the vast majority of your patients can be met. Establish a goal to not have patients walk out your door not accepting and receiving treatment because they can't afford it. There are financial options available today that meet the needs of most people, and at the same time these options are a benefit to the practice. You get paid, but the patient is not financially burdened (refer to Chapter 12).

When you carefully determine a person's perceived and clinical needs through tedious diagnosis and treatment planning, and make the financing of the dentistry comfortable for the patients and for you, you will be meeting the emotional needs of your patients. The three go hand in hand—professional, financial, and emotional. It takes careful and caring communication to accomplish this trilogy of service.

5. Spend time during your evaluation and consultation to educate patients about the recommended treatment

Be sure that they have bought into the treatment plan before you proceed. Involve the patient with the decision-making process so they are clear about the treatment and will feel *essential* to the co-diagnosis process.

The new patient experience, comprehensive oral evaluation, and consultation appointment are crucial. The time you spend to establish a relationship with the patient; the effort you put forth to determine the patient's perceived need, as well as clinical need; and the care with which you deliver your presentation, will make or break the relationship and will certainly have an impact on whether or not a patient accepts treatment

Careful and sincere attention to detail gives the patient a sense of value, worth, and respect. The respect with which you treat your patients will come back to you in the form of respect that goes far beyond the "title" and "degree." It will be a respect that only comes when two people share common concerns and feelings and when they work together to create a solution. You become problem solvers. Problem-solving is a combination of communicative skills.

In today's healthcare world, patients want to be respected. They are looking for the person and the team who will give them the time to listen and to explain so questions are not left unanswered. The listening and speaking skills you will learn in this book are essential to problem-solving. They will enhance your patient relationships and will assist you on your journey of becoming a people professional.

6. Ensure that continuity of information is evident

All team members must be on the same wavelength and must be sending the same messages. An understanding of the services rendered must be an ongoing part of the education of the entire team. Proper verbal skills must be designed, practiced, and implemented so that everyone is saying the same thing with conviction.

This consistency must be evident whether a patient is in the clinical area or in the business area. The business team must give backup support for the clinical team and vice versa.

For example: When a patient asks the business administrator, "Do I really need this?", affirmative encouragement and relevant information must be given. In order to do this, the business administrator must know what is going on, why it is going on, what the benefits to the patient will be, and what the risks might be should the patient decide not to proceed. This third party reinforcement can be very important in the patient's decision-making process. Remember—people look toward all members of the team as the professionals, and as such, they want and need your advice, your answers, and your encouragement. They want to know, "Am I making the right decision?" They are asking for help. Give it consistently.

If there are any areas of discussion or treatment that can (legally) be performed by an auxiliary person, then provide the necessary instruction, education, and practice to raise their confidence level and the confidence level of the doctor. When patients receive consistent, quality care from all members of the team (not just the doctor), they feel totally confident and will develop an even greater bond to the practice. In addition, consistency of discussion and information throughout the entire team nurtures security on the part of the patient.

We call this *linkage communication*—the consistent communication between and among team members. Patients are confused by receiving mixed or different messages. Repetition is the key to learning, so when all team members are on the same wavelength and are mutually supportive of a patient's education—clarity results. When clarity and understanding are established, the likelihood of treatment acceptance is accelerated.

7. Make sure—without compromise—that the completion of treatment obtains excellent results

Let the patient become overtly aware of the success of the treatment, both verbally and visually. Take before and after photographs with a 35mm, a digital, or an intra oral camera to capture before and after photographs of every single case you perform. These before and after photographs are not only educational, but they will also validate the excellent results of treatment to you and your patients.

In addition, digital radiography gives you diagnostic and evaluative capability that is unparalleled. Utilize this new high-tech equipment to:

- diagnose more thoroughly and comprehensively,
- evaluate your own work, and
- give the patient visual evidence of the excellent results of treatment.

Also, seeing the results of the completed treatment will offset buyer's remorse if the patient is wondering why they invested so much money in their dental care.

Express your satisfaction with the results of treatment. (Backup support by the entire team is valuable here.) Talk about the treatment and the positive end result. The patients will be reinforced to know that you are proud of the results.

8. Be willing to stand behind all treatment

Assure the patients that you are always there to answer questions and support the treatment that you have provided and they have received. This commitment to the results will go a long way to build the person's confidence in you. They will know that if you are willing to stand behind your treatment, you will do the very best job the first time. In addition, if something does go wrong, or if questions do arise, they will not feel stranded.

9. Stay in contact with your patient family in a positive way on a regular basis

Be sure they hear from you through verbal and written contact (Refer to Fig. 10-4). When people think of the dentist, you want them to think of you in a positive way, not as the person who hurts them, the person they only hear from when there is money due, or the last person in the world they would want to see.

Change the historical view of the dentist. Become pro-active in your own way to change the patient's perception of who you are and what you do. Inform your patient family about the new and exciting things happening in dentistry today. Be excited about the possibilities. The more you are excited about new advances and opportunities, the more excited your patient family will become. Don't count on the outside world to educate your patients about dental advancements. You must accept the role of educator and assume the responsibility for this process.

In surveys by the American Dental Association, four major factors emerge as deterrents to people seeking and accepting dental care. Those four factors are as follows:

- No perceived need—lack of dental education
- Fear of the cost
- Fear of the dentistry itself
- Time—convenience

If lack of dental education is the dominant reason why people either don't go to the dentist in the first place or don't say "yes" to your recommendations, then it makes good sense to become great educators of dentistry. Become teachers. Learn the different personality styles so you can individualize your instruction. Gear your presentation to the needs of each unique individual. Use excellent presentation skills (refer to Chapter 10), and have fun with the educational process.

Education is impacted by all four of the communication skills—reading, writing, speaking, and listening. The following list identifies the percentage of use for each of the four communication skills in daily interactions:

Reading   16%

Writing   9%

Speaking   35%

Listening   40%

All are critical to the educational process. However, most people will agree that listening may be the most essential communication skill of all. You will need all four communication skills to properly and effectively educate, and you will need to incorporate multiple types of educational tools to enhance the learning process.

Taking time and applying excellent care to your educational processes will lift you up in the eyes of your patients and will enhance your patient care to the nth degree. Great people skills!

10. Always provide the kind of quality care set forth in your statement of mission and detailed in your "vision."

Everyone on the team must be consistent in all that is done. Have all of your management systems in alignment, and make sure they are functioning well. Study and practice communication skills so you can accurately determine the needs of your patients and deliver your messages in a clear and understandable manner.

Give your patients what they want, need, and expect. Then, give a little more. Always give more than is expected. It is the little extras that will set you apart. Together, as a team, write out a scenario of what you think would be the ideal appointment for a patient. (Make sure the scenario reflects what your patients have told you they want.) Then design a plan of action as to how to make that happen every time. You want people walking out of your door thinking that they have never had such a positive dental experience in their life!

Once you have designed the plan, consistently put it into action every time with every patient. People must not wonder what is going to happen in the office. They must be confident and sure of what will happen. Make sure that the "happening" is fabulous!

Do all that is expected, and a little bit more, every time!

In Summary

Becoming a devoted and excellent people professional is fun! Your patients will confidently come to you, look forward to their time with you instead of dreading to come to the dentist, and will appreciate what you are doing for them. You will receive many more "thank yous" when you provide care that is above and beyond the expected.

Remember this valuable management principle. It is the basis of people professionalism. Indeed, it is "better to give than to receive." When you are in the business of giving your patients service based on quality, sincerity, excellence, and going the extra mile, you will feel good about your work and so will your patients. The rewards for being people professionals are personal and professional fulfillment as well as financial fulfillment.

UNDERSTANDING
PERSONALITY DIFFERENCES

*Temperament is the combination of traits
we were born with; character is our "civilized"
temperament; and personality is the "face"
we show to others.*

— DR. TIM LAHAYE

*I*n order to function effectively with the majority of people, you must learn and apply three functions—flexibility, versatility, and adjustability. Being flexible, versatile, and adjustable makes it possible not only for you to appreciate the differences among people, but also to deal successfully with the uniqueness of individuals. You are not going to change people, nor would you want to do so. Your challenge is to adapt to individual differences so that you get along and have successful relationships.

Understanding the differences in personality, appreciating those differences, and knowing how to adapt so as to relate more effectively to an individual can lead to better problem-solving, clearer and more enjoyable relationships, and greater case acceptance.

Personality Differences

Misunderstanding of or a lack of appreciation for personality differences can be overcome if a study and an acceptance of the variances between and among people is pursued. More than 2,000 years ago, Hippocrates determined that there are four basic temperaments among men and women. According to Hippocrates, the four basic personality temperaments or personality styles are as follows:

Choleric   the driving personality that wants results and control

Sanguine   the enthusiastic personality that wants attention and positive "strokes"

Melancholy   the congenial personality that wants compatibility and harmony

Phlegmatic   the steady personality that wants structure and organization

Each of your patients or teammates is unique. Treating each of them in exactly the same manner, or presenting your recommendations in the same manner, is ineffective.

As a dental professional, your responsibility is to teach people about the following:

- The needs in their oral cavity
- The steps they need to take to regain health or change their smile and why
- What procedures you offer to meet those needs
- The benefits of receiving the treatment
- The financial responsibility

In order to meet these objectives and to achieve a high learning curve with your patient-students, excellent teaching must take place. One of the foundational principles of education is that you can't teach everyone in exactly the same manner. Different people learn in different ways. Thus, individualizing your instruction is critical.

The first step in being able to individualize is to identify each of the personality types or temperaments and to have a basic understanding of each. Then you can adjust your presentation modality or approach to each individual. Individualization can begin. The end result will be that more people will accept your treatment recommendations, and less conflict and fewer difficulties will erupt.

CHARACTERISTICS
OF THE FOUR PERSONALITY STYLES

Choleric

Desires authority and prestige, takes a logical approach, likes a decision to be their own. To relate most effectively with the choleric, you need to do the following:

- Be brief and to the point. They want direct answers
- Stick to the business at hand
- Outline the possibilities
- Stress the logic of their decision
- If time is an issue, give them a time frame, but stress the benefits and end results of the treatment plan

Sanguine

Cares about appearance, desires social recognition, likes to be recognized for their abilities. To relate most effectively with the sanguine, you need to do the following:

- Provide a friendly environment
- Let them express their likes and dislikes. Listen to them
- Show before and after photos or testimonials of others who have had the same treatment
- Give them a written treatment plan. They want reassurance.
- Use the intra-oral camera or imaging system
- They want to feel respected and feel a part of the decision
- Stress positives of going ahead with treatment

Melancholy

Likes the status quo, wants security of a situation, needs time to think about a decision, wants to be appreciated, likes to identify with others, feels most comfortable with a specific pattern of treatment. In order to relate most effectively with the melancholy, you need to do the following:

- Provide a sincere, caring, agreeable environment
- Show sincere interest in him/her as a person
- Get their opinion by asking open-ended questions
- Be patient. They may not be sure what they want
- Give them a chance to adjust
- Define specifically what is going to happen
- Give them assurance and support
- Emphasize how going ahead will minimize the risk of getting worse

Phlegmatic

Likes security, no sudden changes, personal attention, little responsibility, and exact definition of their responsibilities, if any. They like a controlled environment and reassurance. In order to relate most effectively with the phlegmatic, you need to do the following:

- Take time to prepare in advance for any presentation
- Give straight pros and cons
- Reassure—no surprises
- Give exact details and precise explanations
- Provide a step-by-step approach to reach the goal
- If disagreeing, disagree with facts, not the person
- Be prepared to explain, over and over again

HOW TO ADJUST
TO THE PERSONALITY DIFFERENCES

Let's take a situation and apply the knowledge of personality differences. In this way, you can see how the adjustments will be of benefit to you.

Situation. The patient comes in for a new patient experience and a comprehensive oral evaluation. You provide that evaluation and invite the patient back to your office for a consultation appointment. The four following scenarios reflect an understanding of personality differences and how an interaction might vary depending on the personality style of the patient.

If you present your recommendations in exactly the same way to each of the four personality temperaments, three of them will probably go away! If you don't adjust your methods of communication relating well to all of your patients, they will not understand, nor will they see the benefits and the relevancy of your recommendations. View an understanding of personality differences as a forward step in your efforts to enhance your people skills and effective communication. Remember what John Rockefeller said: "85% of your success will be your people skills, while 15% of your success will be your technical skills."

Patient #1: Ms. Choleric

1. Have the following ready for her arrival:

- A written treatment plan
- Clear, written financial information
- Visual aids
- Scheduling alternatives
- Be well prepared for the presentation

2. Opening statement:

> **Doctor:** *"Ms. Choleric, last week when you were here for your evaluation appointment, I asked you to tell me what your goals were for your teeth, your mouth, and your smile. You were very clear about your goals. I listened well and*

took notes during our conversation. During the past week, I have reviewed all of the diagnostic data and have designed a treatment plan to help you reach the goals that you have defined for me."

3. Present your recommendations quickly.

Give specific ramifications: how long it will take, the number of appointments, etc. Show her examples of similar situations so she can see the results of the recommended procedures. However, don't show too many examples, and be brief with the ones you do have. Give the financial responsibilities, close, and schedule the first appointment.

Be sure to let her know that you will provide as much treatment as possible at each appointment because you understand the intensity of her schedule.

4. Ask her if she has any questions or if you have responded to her requests adequately.

Make sure that she knows that you have heard her, that you respect her right to make her own decision, and that you are a vehicle for her to reach her goals.

Remember: be brief, to the point, direct, focused. The choleric:

- is goal-oriented—let her know you are in the business of meeting her goals. She likes to be in charge and run the show—make her think that she is in charge and you are there to help
- is strong-willed and decisive—let her be involved with the decision-making process. In fact, let her feel as if the decision is totally hers. You will get a lot further

Patient #2: Ms. Sanguine

1. Be ready for her arrival by doing the following:

- Make sure you are totally prepared for her consultation. Have her greeted by someone she knows, perhaps a treatment coordinator who was with her during her first appointment with you. Spend a bit of time with her during the beginning of the appointment to make her feel special and comfortable.

- Have the written treatment plan available along with appropriate visual aids. If you have an intra-oral camera, have it in the consultation room with her full-face image on the screen when she walks into the room

- Be prepared to show her before and after photographs of people who have received the same kind of treatment she is seeking

- Have testimonial letters from satisfied patients who have received similar treatment

- Use an imaging system to show her how beautiful she will look with the change

2. Opening statement:

Doctor: *Ms. Sanguine, how are you today? (Then be a good listener.) We're glad you are here today. I want you to know that I listened very carefully last week as we discussed your particular situation and your particular concerns. We took careful notes so I could design a treatment plan that would meet your specific needs.*

I know you are uncomfortable with your smile right now. Please know that we will work with you until we achieve the smile you want. In fact, Ms. Sanguine, I want to show you some situations that are similar to yours— people who were not pleased with their smiles and who are happy now as a result of receiving the kind of treatment that I am going to recommend to you today.

This person had a situation similar to yours (show the before photographs or images). Her front teeth had a space between them, and they were somewhat discolored. Can you see the similarity of this person's smile to yours?

Once we completed her treatment, she looked like this (show the after photographs or images). What do you think? (Wait for a response.) Ms. Sanguine, I feel confident telling you that once we complete your treatment, you will look similar to this. What do you think? (Again, wait for her response—you could do cosmetic imaging here, as well.)

3. Then go into a discussion on treatment recommendations.

However, be sure not to get too technical or too detailed. This patient wants to know what she will look like, if she will be comfortable during treatment, and if people will like her new smile. She is not interested in how many millimeters you will be removing or what wonderful technique you will be using. In fact, if you get too technical with this patient, she will not be able to make a decision. She will walk out of your door, and you will wonder, "What ever happened to good 'ole Ms. Sanguine?"

4. When you are discussing financial arrangements, be sure to reinforce the excellent decision that she is making.

Give her permission to spend money on herself. Let her know that she will be pleased, and that the people in her life will be pleased with the results. Ask her if she has any questions. Give her a card with a personally written note or name on it so she can call with any questions.

5. Send her home with a coffee mug or other gift.

Thank her for her time and her confidence in you. Be sure to write her a personal note of thanks. Once her treatment is completed, write her another note of thanks, and send a before and after photograph to her at her place of employment (Fig. 4-1). If she wants to tuck it away, she can. Even if she chooses to do this, you will be reinforcing her excellent decision to receive treatment. However, more than likely, this exuberant personality will want to show other people her results. She will talk about you because that is her nature. She will become an ambassador for your practice.

Remember: Be friendly, congenial, and show her lots of attention. The sanguine:

- is talkative—ask open-ended questions to get to the bottom of her perceived needs
- is enthusiastic and expressive—show her some beautiful before and after photographs to capture that enthusiasm

- is gregarious—appeal to her concern about appearance and about being socially acceptable

Patient #3: Mr. Melancholy

1. Have the following ready for his arrival:

Upon confirming the appointment, be sure to let him know that the doctor has reserved special time for him, and that he will receive 100% of the doctor's attention. Have the written treatment plan ready for him and for the discussion. Greet him pleasantly and make sure that you make note of something personal about him. Make notes during your initial interview about his personal situation and bring up something upon his return. He will appreciate your remembrance and will feel special and valued.

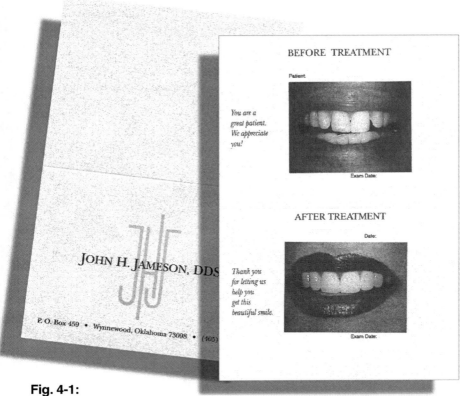

Fig. 4-1:
Personal Note of Thanks

2. Opening statement of the initial interview:

Doctor: *"Mr. Melancholy, if you were to tell me what your goals are for your mouth, your teeth, and your smile what would those goals be?" Then listen carefully. Have an auxiliary take notes so you do not take any of your attention away from him. Body language is critical. He must have excellent rapport with you and have confidence in your personal and professional skills before he will move ahead with treatment.*

Opening statement of the consultation:

Doctor: *"Mr. Melancholy, last week when you came for your evaluation, we gathered a great deal of data about your particular situation. You defined your goals for me at that appointment, and during the past week, I have carefully evaluated the data and have designed a treatment plan that will let you accomplish your goals. Today, I would like to explain that treatment plan to you and would like to discuss the possibilities, so both of us are clear and confident that our work together will meet your needs. Would that be okay with you?" (Get his permission to proceed.)*

3. Then carefully discuss the following:

- What he has now
- What you need to do to help him reach his goals
- What the benefits of treatment will be
- What the problems might be if he does not proceed with treatment
- The financial responsibilities

4 Ask for questions.

Be careful about body language. Do not seem as if you are in a hurry. Give him time to think and ask questions. He will need reassurance. Before and after photographs or images are again significant for validation with this patient.

5. Then if there are no further questions, ask if there is any reason why you should not proceed with treatment.

Open the door for him to voice any concerns, barriers, or objections. If you do not get these out in the open, and if you do not have a chance to discuss these barriers, he will not proceed. Give him a copy of the treatment plan and brochures specifically related to his situation. You could also give him a copy of his before photographs, along with a before and after photograph of a similar situation. (Obviously you would always obtain written permission from any patient before you use their photography for educational purposes.)

If he doesn't schedule his first appointment, ask his permission to call within a week or so to answer any questions he might have related to the treatment.

6. Be patient with this person.

He will come around. It is just going to take a little time. He needs lots of reassurance and supportive material and information.

Remember: Pay attention to detail, be serious, appeal to his intelligence. The melancholy:

- is thoughtful—give him time. Don't push
- likes lists, graphs, and details—give him a written treatment plan with a written financial arrangement. The computerized PowerPoint presentations are terrific for this person
- is a perfectionist—make sure that you give him a sense of security about the treatment he will be receiving. Let him know that you will work with him until you get it right

Patient #4: Mr. Phlegmatic

1. Have ready for his arrival:

As with all personality styles and patients, be exceptionally prepared for the appointment before the patient arrives. The phlegmatic doesn't like surprises, so you need to be ready to present all aspects of the treatment and answer many questions. He is not questioning you, he is just asking for help in making a decision. He needs reassurance.

2. Opening statement of the consultation:

> **Doctor:** *"Mr. Phlegmatic, I've taken quite a bit of time over the last week to review the data we gathered. I wanted to be able to give you a clear picture of what you have now and what I am recommending as far as treatment. I'm going to get right to the point, and I'm going to tell you what I see as your major areas of concern. Then, I will discuss what we need to do to restore your mouth to health again."*

3. Then proceed with your explanation, much as you did with Mr. Melancholy. Detail the following:

- What he has now
- What you need to do to help restore his mouth to health again
- What the benefits of treatment will be
- What the problems might be if he does not proceed with treatment
- The financial responsibilities

In your presentation to Mr. Phlegmatic, be sure to give the pros and the cons of treatment. He wants to know all the details. He wants and needs reassurance and wants no surprises—clinically or financially. Define and present your treatment recommendations in a step-by-step manner. Using a written treatment plan, determine what you need to do, how many appointments, the sequence of them, and how long each appointment will be. Then, detail the fee for the total treatment, what his financial responsibility will be, and the payment method. Write the agreement. Give him a copy, and you keep a copy for your record.

Remember: Be gentle. The phlegmatic is low-key and easy-going.

If you are of the high strung nature, soften. Slow your speech. Be an encourager.

- The phlegmatic may seem uninterested, but keep encouraging.
- He may be shy and is probably indecisive.
- You will need to give strong support for your proposal.
- Be assertive in asking him for a commitment to move ahead. That's okay. He may want you to make the decision for him and then be prepared to support him.

IN SUMMARY

Study the different personality styles. Know that one is not better than another. There are simply differences. Understanding those differences gives you the opportunity to relate better to each unique individual. Wouldn't you agree that relating better to a patient will give them a greater sense of security and trust with you?

In addition, understanding the differences and gaining the ability to be flexible will give you a much broader base from which to work. You will not change anyone. You cannot, nor would you want to change a person's personality. You, however, can adapt your own behavior and get along much better, present more effectively, and establish much stronger relationships. When a person feels understood, he/she feels valued. When a person feels valued, he/she will be more likely to make a commitment to you. Commitment means long-term relationships, working together to find solutions, trusting each other, and feeling confident with decisions made in harmony.

Understanding personality differences is a major step toward gaining greater acceptance of your treatment recommendations. This understanding is foundational to great communication.

LISTEN YOUR WAY TO SUCCESS: REFINING THE ART AND SCIENCE OF LISTENING

One friend, one person who is truly understanding, who takes the trouble to listen to us as we consider our problem, can change our whole outlook on the world

— DR. ELTON MAYO

*L*isten your way to success? How? How can this simple tool be considered the number one management tool in business today? How can listening effectively make a positive difference in your dental practice?

Lee Iacocca believes that "listening can make the difference between a mediocre company and a good company." Mark McCormack, author of *What They Didn't Teach You At Harvard Business School*, feels that "in selling there is no greater asset." Sperry, one of America's major companies, considers the skill of listening so important to the success of their business that they have devoted extensive time and funds to the development of courses for the instruction of listening. They have made these courses available for all levels of personnel. Sperry believes the inability to listen leads to such business inefficiencies as:

- wasted time
- ineffective operation of the departments
- miscarried plans
- frustrated decisions in every phase of the business

There are four operations involved in communication through words: writing, reading, speaking, and listening. When asked, "Which of these four operations is the most significant for effective communication to take place?" most people will say, without hesitation, "listening." Yet most people feel listening is the least developed and the least well performed of the four communicative operations.

Listening needs to be more than an activity of the ear in order to be effective. It needs to be an activity of the mind. There are important differences between hearing and listening. Hearing is the ability to receive the sound vibrations that are transmitted. Listening is making sense out of what you hear.

WHAT IS LISTENING?

Listening, according to Webster, is

- paying attention to sound
- hearing with thoughtful attention

Listening, according to Kevin Murphy, President of CDK Management and Consulting Associates, is:

- the accurate perception of what is being communicated
- a process in perpetual motion

- a two-way exchange in which both parties involved must always be receptive to the thoughts, ideas, and emotions of the other

Mr. Murphy notes, "Listening is a natural process that goes against human nature!"

Effective listening stimulates the team to generate additional creativity, solve problems, and execute smoother systems. In addition, effective listening enables you to become aware of the needs and desires of your patients so you can meet those needs.

LISTENING LEADS TO GREATER TEAMWORK AND BETTER PATIENT RELATIONSHIPS.

In order for you to become a better listener, you first have to see the benefit of that improvement. Place a checkmark by each statement that indicates a reason why you would like to be a better listener.

- ☐ Improve communication
- ☐ Stay in control of a situation
- ☐ Have less frequent arguments
- ☐ Demonstrate a more caring attitude
- ☐ Make fewer mistakes
- ☐ Reduce tension and stress in the practice
- ☐ Improve my memory
- ☐ Better understand the needs of the patients
- ☐ Establish and maintain better relationships with the patients
- ☐ Relate better to my teammates
- ☐ Relate better to my employer/employees

Now evaluate the things that you have checked. Based on your responses, you probably agree with me that working at improving the skill of listening will be a benefit to you and to each and every person you encounter in the practice and at home.

Fig. 5-1: Becoming a Better Listener—An Exercise

The team is the lifeblood and the heart beat of the dental practice. If, as the leader of the team, the dentist realizes this fact, taps the incredible resources he or she has available within the team and genuinely listens to each member of that team, success will be realized.

Pooling the vast resources available on a dental team does the following:

- Helps the dentist focus on multiple sources of information
- Helps the dentist to be a better employer and leader
- Helps the dentist to be a more successful business person

Ultimately, the patients benefit from excellent listening skills since individual and unique needs, fears, concerns, and wants are truly *heard*. Only when you truly listen to these needs will you have the opportunity to do something to satisfy them.

By listening to your patients, you will learn how they feel about your service. You will learn what it is they want. Then you will be able to respond. That's what customer service is all about—defining the needs and meeting them. The only way to determine a person's wants and/or needs is to ask questions and listen. The patient wins by having necessary or desired treatment rendered, and the dental team wins with increased productivity.

WHAT GETS IN THE WAY OF EFFECTIVE LISTENING IN THE DENTAL OFFICE?

Some of the main deterrents to good listening may be:

- time pressure
- stress—not being able to relax
- mindset—being rigid in thought processes
- talking too much—dominating the conversation as the "authority"
- thinking what to say in response instead of listening
- lack of interest
- ego—"I know the answer" or "I know what to do, so I don't need to listen to you"
- interruptions

- distractions
- lack of focus

Before you can learn how to listen effectively, you must develop an understanding of the attitudes necessary for this type of listening to take place. "A mind is like a parachute. It only works when it's open!" An open mind is necessary for the skill of listening to be effective.

WHAT ATTITUDES ARE REQUIRED FOR SUCCESSFUL LISTENING TO OCCUR?

- **You must want to hear what the other person is saying.** Adopt a positive learning attitude. You can improve your listening skill if you want to do so. Listening is a skill, and skills are learned. It may be the attitude that is more difficult to get into proper alignment. If you want to be a better listener and want to improve your relationships with team members as well as with patients, you have to make a decision to do so. The making of the decision is step one on your path to improvement. Realize that no one is a perfect communicator, and no one is a perfect listener. But, if you feel that listening is a valuable communicative skill, then your commitment to further study, practice, and improvement will prove beneficial.

- **You must have the time to listen**. If you don't, schedule a better time. Listening takes time! If you don't have the time, be respectful and say so. It is better to be honest with a person and schedule a time when you can really focus. This is better than pretending you are listening, but in actuality you are nervous about spending the time or are so preoccupied that you aren't hearing a single word.

For example: "Mary, I understand that you have a concern about the late hours we've been keeping! I want very much to hear what you have to say, the suggestions you have, etc., but this is not a good time for such an important discussion. Could we get together tomorrow for lunch and concentrate on this issue uninterrupted?"

- **You must sincerely want to help the other person with the problem**. If you don't want to help, wait until you do!

For example: "Sherry, I realize that the summer is a difficult time for you because your kids are home from school. However, right now, changing schedules is not a possibility, so let's table this discussion until next month."

Note: If you do tell a team member that you will get together later for the continuation of a discussion, then do so! It will be detrimental to your relationship to say you will deal with something and then let it slip away. Respect will deteriorate.

- **You must be able to accept the other person's true feelings.** Other people will have feelings different from yours. Sometimes these feelings may be different from what you think they should be! Learning to accept these differences and not letting that difference affect your relationship takes time and effort—it is not easy.

For example:

Ms. Patient: "I hate the dentist! I only come when I have to!"

Assistant: "I understand that you have some apprehension about the treatment you are going to receive, Ms. Patient, but I want you to know that Dr. Best is great! He is committed to gentle, caring dentistry. We are going to help you understand the treatment, so you will not feel so apprehensive about your time spent with us."

This patient felt differently about dentistry than the team member. However, this difference in feeling did not change the assistant's commitment to educating the patient about good dental care, nor did this difference in feeling about the dental experience negatively affect her attitude about the patient.

- **You must trust that the other person has the ability to handle his/her feelings and can deal with or work through the given situation.** When a person comes to you and expresses a concern or a problem, they may not be asking for your advice. They may need your attention and a place to "vent." Most people do a sensational job of closing the doors to effective listening. They do so by throwing up barriers.

Barriers to listening prevent a person from giving you further information, which is the total opposite of what you want. When a person begins telling you something, you need as much information as possible. Information allows you to identify motivators, problems, concerns, or emotions. Barriers to good listening are numerous. A few are listed below:

- Giving advice
- Offering a solution
- Passing out orders or directives
- Presenting an ultimatum
- Preaching or teaching
- Being critical
- Flattering
- Putting the other person down for his/her thoughts
- Patronizing
- Making fun of the person or making a joke of his/her problem
- Changing the subject
- Talking about your own situation

By practicing excellent listening, you allow another person to deal with his/her own issues. They can clarify some of the questions that may exist. No one can solve a problem except the person who has the problem. Listening leads the way to defining the issue so that successful problem-solving can take place.

Don't take away from a person's ability to deal with his/her own issues. Be an enhancer. Listen without judgment. Allow a person to have separate feelings from you, and allow that person to deal with his/her own emotionality.

Often, listening to a person lets them get something out on the table. That may be all that is necessary. He/she is probably not looking for a solution from you, but rather a sounding board. Know that if someone wants your opinion, he/she will ask for it.

- **You must know that, many times, feelings are transitory.** Be accepting of the human nature of the changing feelings.

For example: A member of your team may be suffering from burnout. She may say she wants to quit, that she isn't happy or satisfied any longer.

Be patient. Listen. Respect the person enough to allow her to express her concerns. Determine if the problem is worthy of solution, or if it is over. If there is a willingness to work on problem-solving, develop a plan of resolution together. The feelings may be transitory. A quality team member is too valuable to release because of a transitory emotional or physical state. Don't make judgments about this person based on your automatic reaction. Take the time to truly define the problem, design a plan for its resolution, and implement the solution. Many emotions are transitory. Accept the humanism of this fact.

- **You must be able to actually listen without becoming self-stimulated or defensive.** Allow for "separateness". The other person is unique from you and responds in his/her own way. Respect this difference.

For example: Often, when we hear what another person is saying to us, we become defensive, and thus close the door to good communication. A more effective way to truly listen to another is to reflect back to the person what we think they are saying in order to get to the center of the message— what the sender really means.

Saying nothing at all *does* communicate acceptance if you are truly listening attentively. Silence is a nonverbal message and, when used effectively, can make a person feel genuinely accepted.

CHALLENGING LISTENING BEHAVIORS

Imagine that the doctor has just given you an assignment. She wants a report of the effectiveness of her case presentations so far this year—how much dentistry has been diagnosed and how much has been accepted. As the doctor is explaining what is wanted in this report, there are five different things that could happen to get in the way of accurate listening.

(1) **Miss what the person is saying.** If you are distracted emotionally or physically, you may not be focused on what is being

said, and you could miss critical aspects of the explanation. For example, if you have a headache, or if you are having difficulties at home, or if you just had a disagreement with a team member, you may not be able to catch everything you're being told. Focus is critical for effective listening.

(2) Misunderstandings. You may hear the words that are being said, but you may be unable to understand the message. For example: You may not have produced this report before, and when the doctor starts to describe what is required, confusion may result. If you are confused, your mind will stay on the point you are trying to figure out and may miss the next point. In a tedious conversation where every detail is important, missing one point may make it impossible to piece together the remainder of the conversation.

(3) Misinterpretation. Language can only represent what a person is thinking or feeling. What someone says to you may mean one thing to him or her and a totally different thing to you. For example: The doctor may indicate that this report will be easy to access and simple to decipher. However, your interpretation of easy and simple may be based on parameters that are not the same as those of the doctor.

(4) Mental change. You may hear the doctor accurately, but as the week progresses and the activities and demands of the week pile up, your mind may play games with you! You may have heard the doctor say she wanted the report by the 5th of the next month, but as time progresses, you think you heard that it was due on the 15th.

(5) Forgetfulness. You may actually hear the doctor say that she wants the report on the 5th, but by the end of your meeting with her, you may have unconsciously forgotten that this deadline was given to you at all. If, during the meeting, several topics or issues were discussed, and if your mind was placed on overload, you may be looking her right in the eye; you might respond affirmatively to her statement about the deadline; and you might give her the impression you are okay with that deadline. However, once your mind goes on overload, the chances of you forgetting are increased.

A CLOSER LOOK AT LISTENING SKILLS

Dr. Thomas Gordon, in his outstanding work on communication skills, teaches that listening skills are necessary to help another person when he/she has a problem. There are four types of listening skills:

- Body language
- Tone of voice
- Passive listening
- Active listening

Let's look at all four.

Body language

Research has shown that approximately 60% of the perception of a message, whether it is being sent or received, depends on body language. One must pay close attention to and carefully plan the physical messages being sent and received. You can make or break a conversation or a presentation by your body language. In fact, even if all of the words are great, the message can come across incorrectly as a result of body language.

Positive body language that you can use to express an attentive, listening posture are:

- Establishing and maintaining eye contact
- Positioning yourself on an equal level
- Staying face to face
- Touching—firmly, but gently
- Nodding or shaking your head
- Facial expressions
- Reflecting a person's body movements

- Taking an open stance with arms and legs (not crossing or closing yourself off)

In being receptive to a person's comfort or understanding, there are numerous body languages that you can observe from the patient:

- Crossed stance with arms and legs
- Clutching the arms of the chair
- Frowning and other facial expressions
- Gestures of the hand/body
- Posture
- Touching behavior
- Physical distance
- Skin responses—blushing, pallor

Do your patients send messages to you via body language? The answer to this question is a resounding "yes." Truly, actions speak louder than words. Be aware of body language cues sent by clients/patients. They can tell you a great deal about the attitude toward your presentation.

The following are body language cues to watch for, what those cues might suggest, and how you can effectively respond to those cues:

Cue—The patient's hands are open and relaxed with palms turned upward. The patient shrugs his/her shoulders in response to your question or statement.

Indication—Open to your recommendations, ready to work with you.

Your response—Proceed and mirror their actions.

Cue—No eye contact.

Indication—Not comfortable with you or with something you've just said. May be intimidated by or feel insecure with you.

Your response—Repeat your last comment or statement. Tell the person that you want to take care of him/her. Try to relax the patient; smile softly at them. Gently but firmly, touch their shoulder or arm, and ask if what you have just said bothers them.

Cue—Patient leans toward you or moves a little closer.

Indication—Trust is being established. They are beginning to accept what you are telling them.

Your response—Ask questions to see if they are beginning to accept your recommendations (e.g., Chewing better is what you want, isn't it?).

Cue—Patient is looking directly at you and giving you his/her full attention. Touches chin or side of face.

Indication—Very receptive. Giving thoughtful consideration.

Your response—Continue. Go on. Proceed.

Cue—Takes glasses off and wipes the lenses.

Indication—Thinking it over.

Your response—Slow down. You are moving too fast. Reiterate and clarify your last point. Recap the points you've already agreed upon.

Cue—Eyebrows raise, forehead wrinkles, mouth falls open.

Indication—Shock or surprise.

Your response—Ask questions to find out if the surprise is positive or negative (i.e., Doctor: "From the look on your face, I sense that you are surprised. Are you?" Patient: "Yes. I'm very surprised!" Doctor: "Surprised in what way and about what issue?")

If the response is positive, proceed! Help him/her to get even more excited. If the response is negative, calm them down. Reassure them.

Cue—Pulls on ear while you are talking.

Indication—Wants to break in to ask a question or make a point.

Your response—Pause. Ask if they have a comment or question.

Cue—Hand covers mouth.

Indication—Insecure, self -doubt, self-conscious.

Your response—Reassure. Go back and clarify points you've already made.

Cue—Squirming in chair

Indication—Feeling pressured or uncomfortable.

Your response—Reflect back to the person what you think they might be feeling. Clarify if your perception is accurate or not. Find out what's making him/her uncomfortable.

Cue—Fidgeting with an article such as a bracelet or watch or pencil. Eyes lowered as you are talking.

Indication—Insecure, lack of confidence.

Your response—Validate the person; positively reinforce them. Explain your recommendations again or in more detail: "Ms. Patient, let me go over my recommendations with you again. That might answer questions you have at this time. Would you like that?"

Don't underestimate the power and significance of these body language messages or sensory perception cues. The acceptance of your recommendations will improve in direct proportion to your ability to relate to and with your patients. Don't miss an opportunity to listen accurately to their body language.

The giving and receiving of messages can be an asset to the total dental experience. You, as a good listener, want to perceive all possible messages. You will then be better able to plan your presentation of recommendations and the treatment itself. The more a patient feels listened to, the more comfortable, relaxed, open, receptive, and less difficult he/she will become.

TONE OF VOICE

Tone of voice and vocal cues account for approximately 30% of the perception of a message, whether you are sending or receiving. Body language accounts for 60% of the message—30% plus 60% is 90%! Obviously, the words you speak are important, but everything else may have a greater impact. When people tell you to choose your words carefully, that's good advice. However, better advice might be to choose the way you say your words carefully.

Vocal cues. There are four kinds of vocal cues: pitch, rate, volume, and quality. Let's look at each of these individually:

Pitch—describes the highness and lowness of your voice. It is determined by your genetic makeup. However, certain things do affect the pitch of your voice such as nervousness, fatigue, emotion, etc.

Rate—indicates how fast or slowly you speak. Rate of speech is a part of your personality makeup; some people who are high energy speak faster. Those who are laid back and more relaxed will often speak more slowly and deliberately. It is commonly known that where you live or were raised can impact your rate of speech: rural versus metropolitan, southern versus northern, etc. In addition, your emotional state affects your rate of speech. If you are nervous or excited, your rate will usually accelerate.

Volume—means the loudness or softness of your voice. Everyone has a volume that is normal for everyday activities. In some cases, volume is related to self-confidence. Softness may indicate shyness, low self-esteem, or fear. However, sometimes a loud, boastful person is actually making an effort to cover up a poor self-esteem. Some people think the louder they speak, the better they will be understood. Know that people do make these kinds of judgments about the message being sent. In some cases, the assumption is totally inaccurate. Thus, paying attention to the volume of your speech can make a difference.

Quality—is the actual sound of your voice. Unless you take voice lessons, you can probably do little about the quality of your voice. However, this is a valuable point. The voice is an instrument; it can be "tuned." If your voice is very deep and resonating, it may be difficult to hear. On the other hand, a nasal, whiny voice may give a negative impression and may be difficult to listen to.

If you are unhappy with the quality of your voice, or if you think you are not making a solid enough impression with your vocal presentation, consider vocal lessons. The voice can be trained. Most people do not have any idea how effective vocal training can be. Controlling the voice by controlling your breathing can improve the quality of your voice, which can improve the delivery of your messages.

In addition to these four vocal cues, the emphasis you place on your individual words can make a big difference in the impact of your message. Here is an exercise to help you see this difference. Deliver the following sentence, emphasizing the underlined word each time. Then, describe how the emphasis changes the meaning of what is being communicated.

- *I* do not want a raise today.
- I *do* not want a raise today.
- I do *not* want a raise today.
- I do not *want* a raise today.
- I do not want *a* raise today.
- I do not want a *raise* today.
- I do not want a raise *today*.

In order to be a better listener, practice these techniques:

- Listen closely to the words being spoken. Make sure you are clear about the message being sent. If you have questions, ask for clarification
- Pay attention to the vocal cues being sent. This will help you understand the emotionality of the message. Remember, excellent communication means paying attention to both the content and the emotion of the message
- If someone is difficult to listen to or if his/her vocal quality leaves something to be desired, you will have to focus more intently. It's easy to drift off when someone's vocal quality is lacking. You must make special effort in these types of listening situations
- Become aware of your own vocal cues. In spite of what you are saying, your body language and your tone of voice will impact the message more significantly than anything else. Be sure that you let both body language and tone of voice work in your favor. Practice may be in order.

Practice improving your tone of voice. When you are speaking, you are actually singing. Your voice is an instrument, and your speech is your song. Most people's vocal range when speaking crosses at least one octave. In speaking versus singing, the notes are not sustained, but rather slide quickly from note to note. A wide range of intonation makes for a more interesting and effective speaking style. A person who stays on the same note is monotonous or monotone, which means one note. An important aspect of speech is changing the intonation, meaning to add variety to your words.

A good way to check out your own intonation style and variety is to close your mouth and speak as you would normally speak. Just hum your sentences. All you will hear is the intonation. Practice this sentence, "I can't believe I am doing this!" First, say the sentence out loud. Then, close your lips, and hum the sentence. What did you hear? If you heard a flat line of notes with a brief rise in the middle, you could use some coaching! If you heard both a rising and a falling of your voice, terrific! You were musical and interesting in your delivery.

Listen to people on the radio or television who have particularly interesting voices. Realize how captivating they are in their delivery. Practice doing the same thing with your voice. This may seem awkward or artificial to you. That's okay. Remember that you are only practicing. By practicing, you will begin to see slight but effective changes in your every day speech.

Just like any skill, communication needs study, practice, and coaching. Great vocalists have coaches. Great athletes have coaches. Great presenters have coaches. Anyone who excels in any skill practices that skill. They know that nothing is ever perfect, and that constant effort must be put forth for improvement to take place. Communication may be your most important skill. Practice it.

Passive listening

The secret to getting along well with other people is to determine their needs and to be willing to help the person satisfy those needs. How do you find out what those needs might be? Ask open-ended questions that cannot be answered with a "yes" or a "no." Then listen to pick up information that might:

- give you a clue as to what motivates that person
- what they want
- what the possible barriers to acceptance or solution might be

Passive listening responses are non-stimulating responses that encourage a person to continue talking, to go on, to provide you with more information, etc. There are two kinds of passive listening responses—acknowledgments and door openers. An acknowledgment is the simpler of the two. Examples of acknowledgments might be as follows:

"Really?"
"I see."
"Uh huh."
"Hmmm."
"Okay."

Door openers are a bit more specific. A door opener is a statement or question that actually gives the person a directive to keep talking. Examples of door openers might be as follows:

"Tell me how we can help you."
"Tell me about that."
"Give me some more information."
"Go on."
"I'd like to know how you feel about that."
"Please continue."
"Tell me more."

These are ways of listening that encourage a person to continue, to go on, to get it all out. Ask a question, and then respond with a non-stimulating response. This type of receptive listening means that you are attentive and are hearing what the other person is saying, but you are careful not to interfere with their commentary.

Pay attention to the body language with appropriate attending skills. Listen caringly and carefully, allowing the other person to continue without interruption. Don't try to fill all silent moments.

Careful pauses in the conversation give the person time to organize their thoughts, gain the

KEYPOINT:

Silence is a communication skill.

confidence to go on, and express their deeper feelings. Silence can be a form of very powerful communication.

According to Dr. Gordon, "Silence or Passive Listening is a potent tool for getting people to talk about what's bothering them, and talking to someone who is willing to listen may be just the encouragement a person needs to keep going."

The most challenging part of passive listening is asking the question and then waiting for the person to respond without interrupting! When you ask a question, be quiet! Let him/her answer even if a few moments of silence occur.

Active listening

When you have opened the lines of communication and have encouraged a person to continue, the next step is to listen actively. The single most effective listening skill you can use to calm an irate person, to defuse anger, to handle a difficult person, or on the other hand, to enhance a good relationship, is to listen actively or reflectively. This kind of listening requires effort and discipline.

Active listening is "feeding back to the person what you think you have heard him/her saying to make sure that you have heard correctly." A simple repetition or paraphrasing is not sufficient. The listener should demonstrate, in his/her own words, an adequate understanding of the content, intent, and emotion of the speaker's remarks.

Active listening is used when someone comes to you with a problem or a concern. Active listening is the restating in your own words what you understand the other person to be saying. You must give careful attention to both the content of the message and the feeling that is being transmitted.

For example:

Ms. Patient: "At my last dentist's office, I could just pay him after my insurance had paid. I can't believe that you are suggesting that I must pay my portion the day I receive this treatment. This is infuriating!"

Business Administrator: "Ms. Patient, you seem upset because our financial policy is different from the one you are used to."

Ms. Patient: "I am! I don't see any reason to pay anything until I know exactly what my insurance is going to cover."

Business Administrator: "I understand your confusion over the difference, Ms. Patient. Although we file your insurance as a service, you are responsible for the portion that insurance does not cover. Therefore, we ask that you take care of your estimated portion the day of your appointment. We want you to be aware of this before treatment is provided so that there would be no surprises for you following your treatment."

Ms. Patient: "Well, I can appreciate that! So, next week when I come in for my appointment I need to pay \$_____, is that right?"

Business Administrator: "Yes, that is correct. We will file your insurance that day, also. Then, if there is any difference after your insurance pays, we will immediately notify you so that you can take care of that difference."

By using active listening in the beginning of this conversation, the business administrator was able to figure out the problem. She didn't antagonize the patient; that would have led to more anger, a potential scene, and possibly losing a patient.

The following examples will display a message sent by someone who has a problem. The responses that follow are examples of:

(1) a response that is typical and yet acts as a door closer, and then

(2) a response that will illustrate active listening, a true door opener to communication

- **Team member:** "Why does Sarah have to make so many mistakes?"

  Office Manager: "She is having a lot of problems at home. Give her a break!"

  Office Manager: "You seem frustrated by Sarah's performance these days." (active listening)

- **Assistant:** "I'm not sure I'm ready to assist you with that procedure yet."

Doctor: "You can do it if you just try!"

Doctor: "You're uncomfortable because you're unsure of how to perform this procedure." (active listening)

- **Team member:** "I won't ever say anything in a staff meeting again!"

  Other team member: "Well, that wasn't a very good idea you threw out!"

  Other team member: "You feel hurt because you are not sure your ideas are accepted?" (active listening)

In the above examples, the first response would probably not encourage further discussion nor would the response open the door to positive communication. If there was a problem to be solved, the first response did nothing to further the seeking of a solution. However, the second response (active listening) indicates a true acceptance of the person's feelings and an understanding of the content of the message. Now they can go on to the defining and solving of the problem.

When you learn to integrate active listening into your repertoire of communication skills, you truly involve the mind in a dynamic process rather than using only the ears in a physical process. You reach out to the sender of the message with your own message of caring and acceptance.

If you use only your ears to hear the words, but do not use your mind to understand what is really being said and felt, then you do nothing to advance communication. The result is failure to communicate!

From this type of feedback, the sender gets tangible evidence of how the receiver deciphered the message. The sender can either confirm the accuracy of the message ("Yes, that is just what I meant") or deny the accuracy ("No, what I meant was..."). This kind of continual feedback allows you to be absolutely sure that you understand what is being said. This also provides a sense of empathy and acceptance for the one delivering the message.

One of the most important things I have learned about listening, and in particular, active listening, is that you can help a person "de-flood" by listening carefully and caringly to him/her. What do I mean by de-flood? When a person is overwhelmed with emotion, an emotion of any kind, they cannot think clearly. They are said to be emotionally flooded. In order for a person to hold a compatible conversation, to be able to make a logical decision, or to be able to hear what you have to say, he/she must have a balance between intellect and emotion. If a person is flooded with an emotion, intellect gets squashed! You can help a person get back into a state of balance between intellect and emotion by piercing the full balloon of emotion and letting some of it out. You do this by listening (Fig 5-2).

Emotional Flooding

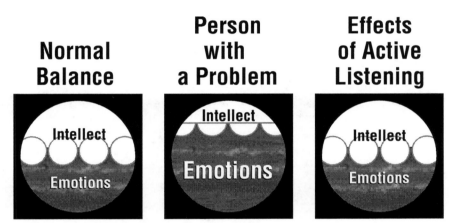

Normal Balance / **Person with a Problem** / **Effects of Active Listening**

Intellect — Emotions

Fig. 5-2: Becoming a Better Listener—Deflooding

One of the main purposes of effective listening is to keep misunderstandings to a minimum. When you are involved in a listening situation, make sure that you do so with sincerity, understanding, acceptance, and caring. Listen to your teammates and to your patients. Open doors to communication!

EIGHT STEPS TO EFFECTIVE LISTENING

- Reduce as many distractions and interruptions as possible
- Focus your mind on the speaker. Clear away as many internal distractions as possible
- Take notes of key issues so you stay focused and can return to these points when appropriate

- Respond to the speaker's total message. Do not pay attention to the words only. Pay attention to the body language, tone of voice, and the emotion
- Listen without judgment
- Do not be thinking about what you are going to say or how you are going to respond. You will be unable to listen accurately
- Keep an open mind when you are listening to another
- If you catch yourself not listening, refocus, and change your body position to make it more conducive to listening

In Summary

You are in the profession of dentistry, and no matter what the specific goals and objectives of your practice, each and every one of your days is an exchange of context and emotion. That is communication, both verbal and non-verbal. If you choose to ignore or underplay this constant exchange of data, you will be missing an incredible opportunity to increase your practice by utilizing numerous information sources, solving everyday problems constructively and painlessly, and drawing upon the talent that penetrates your practice every day!

Put listening, the greatest single management tool you can possess, into effect. Put it to work *for* you! Other successful business leaders have discovered its value. So can you! You will be nurturing the following:

- The creative potential of your employees
- A strong, enthusiastic team
- Patients accepting treatment and optimum dental health
- The reaching of your own potential and the potential of your practice

GETTING YOUR MESSAGE ACROSS IN A POSITIVE WAY: SPEAKING SKILLS

*The meeting of two minds may consist in their
understanding one another while still in disagreement,
or it may consist in their coming into agreement
as a result of their understanding one another.*

— MORTIMER ADLER

*P*aul Harvey says, "It's not what you say, it's how you say it." I totally
agree. So many times we taint our message by interspersing words and
phrases that conjure up a negative response or thought.

As dental professionals, your hearts are in the right place. You want to
help people. You want patients to understand that everything you do is
geared toward better care. Improving your speaking skills can become an
asset to your relationships and to your practice.

THE COMMUNICATION FLOW

Excellent communication takes place between two people when the listener correctly interprets the message sent by the speaker. Obviously both of the skills—listening and speaking—are critical to the flow of communication.

Speaking is a part of the communication flow. Speaking so others will listen to you and so that your message will be understood is a critical part of that process. As stated in Chapter 1, in each and every one of your dental days, all members of the team have "a moment of truth" with a client/patient. In that moment, each team member has a chance to make or break a relationship with a patient. Each interaction is so important. No one person, nor any one interaction, is more important than any other. Respect each interaction, and realize the value of each.

How each team member speaks to the patient can make a difference in whether or not he or she will make a decision to accept treatment. The goal of each member of your team should be to listen well enough to determine the patient's perceived needs and goals and to speak professionally and compassionately so patients understand the benefits of your services and will choose to proceed with treatment.

The goals of good speaking are as follows:

- To help people want to listen to what you have to say
- To deliver the message in the best possible manner
- To check to see if you were heard (or interpreted) correctly

GETTING YOUR MESSAGE ACROSS EFFECTIVELY

There are three specific factors defining whether or not a person will want to listen to the message you are sending. These are as follows:

- Will this benefit me?
- Who's delivering the message?
- How is the message being delivered?

Will this benefit me?

People are motivated by the question "what's in this for me?" People want to know how something will benefit them. Is the information useful, interesting, and productive? If people are told what's good for them, they probably won't buy into it. A person must see the benefits of a product or service and how it will impact them. In other words, people want to know "How does this affect me?"

In order to get a person to the point where they are willing to listen to your proposal, you first have to determine what motivates that person. The only way to determine a person's motivational "hot buttons" is to ask questions and listen. Once you have defined those hot buttons, you are in a position to respond to them.

Make it interesting:

- Ask questions to open the lines of communication
- Determine the motivational "hot buttons"
- Respond to the person's needs in your presentation
- Focus on how the recommended treatment will benefit the person

Who's delivering the message?

Does the person receiving the message trust the person sending the message? Your initial contact with a person is very critical. A person needs to know your intentions before they can or will trust you. People want to know "Are you for me?" "Will you help me?," "What will happen if I trust you?" and "Will you take advantage of me?."

People decide if they trust you in two ways—emotionally and intellectually.

KEYPOINT:

"Tell me and I will forget. Show me and I might remember. Involve me and I will understand."

—*Chinese Proverb*

Even though a person tries to make a decision based on fact, the process is filtered through the emotions.

A level of trust must be established before you can gain another's confidence. Don't underestimate the importance of spending time and giving attention to the building of rapport. The time spent on relationship building may be the best time you spend with a person. You will only go so far with a person unless they are confident in your sincerity and true interest in them. The level and the depth of your relationship will be in direct proportion to that level of trust.

How is the message being delivered?

How do you get your message across to the listener or receiver? As we discussed in Chapter 5, 60% of the perception of a message is sent or received via body language, 30% through the tone of voice, and 10% through the words spoken. The way in which you deliver your message may have more impact on the listener than what you are saying.

In addition, people learn and respond more effectively to visual messages than to auditory messages. Approximately 83% of a person's learning takes place visually. Therefore, supporting your information with visual aids will clarify your message. This allows the listener to be involved with the communication. Involvement is a key to learning and understanding.

There's the goal—to have communication experiences become a mutual involvement of all parties and to have interactions that encourage the giving and receiving of information and feelings. The result? Winning relationships. Strong relationships. Acceptance of treatment proposals.

KEY POINTS OF SPEAKING
SO THAT OTHERS WILL LISTEN

- Be direct—don't beat around the bush
- Be specific—get to the point
- Be positive
- Don't use "put down" language or a patronizing voice
- Learn what motivates the person
- Establish a relationship of trust
- Present your information succinctly and visually
- Involve the person throughout the conversation

HOW TO SEND CLEAR MESSAGES

How you communicate with your patients can be a source of mutual respect and understanding or a source of frustration and discouragement for both of you. Your knowledge and skill of communication are the bottom line for successful relationships.

Effective communication takes place when there is a clear sending of a message (speaking skills) and appropriate feedback to verify the accuracy of the reception (listening skills) (Fig. 6-1). In other words, "Did you get my message?" and "Am I hearing you right?" It is definitely a two-way process.

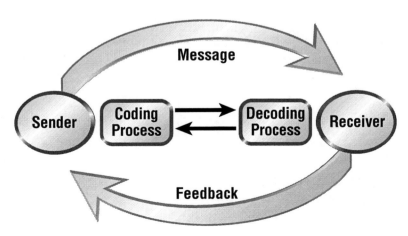

Fig. 6-1: Flow of Communication

A person sends a message either verbally or nonverbally, or both. The message that the speaker wants to convey to the receiver is transformed into outward behavior (verbal or nonverbal).

The message is received by the other person who then interprets it based on prior experience and understanding. Feelings are produced in reaction to the interpretation. Judgments are made about the intention of the message.

Receiving or requesting feedback gives the sender of the message a chance to know if the message has been heard accurately or if it needs clarification. Determine if your message has been sent and received accurately.

For example:

Doctor: "Mrs. Jones, during our initial evaluation, you told me that you wanted to keep your teeth for a lifetime. That's great. We want the same thing for you. Based on my diagnosis and evaluation of your situation, I am going to recommend that we become involved with an active program of periodontal therapy enabling us to get and keep your gum tissue healthy.

Without healthy gum tissue, we cannot restore your teeth to health again. We must have a solid foundation upon which to work. This foundation will secure the investment in time and money that you will be making, and it will serve as security for your health. Getting and keeping a healthy mouth is your major goal, isn't it? If it's okay with you, I would like to explain what is involved in periodontal therapy and how the therapy will benefit you" (explanation follows).

Doctor: "Mrs. Jones, do you have any questions about the therapy I am recommending for you? (Pause for questions.) What aspects of the therapy do you think would be the most beneficial? (Pause.) What areas cause you the most concern?" (Pause.) (The doctor asks for feedback. If the patient is clear about the message he has sent, then the doctor proceeds.)

Incorporate this process in all situations in which it is important that the message you are sending is a clear one and that the person to whom you are speaking has received it properly.

STEPS OF EFFECTIVE SPEAKING AND PRESENTING

Step 1—Use layman's language

You've heard this a million times—because it is so important! Dental professionals often think they are using layman's language when in fact the patient has no idea what was said.

The English language often has multiple meanings for one word. Some words have as many as 25 different meanings. Often, when a dental person is explaining treatment, the person becomes lost and can never really get back on track. The patient may be embarrassed to tell you they do not understand, and so they just say, "Yes, I understand." Then, they leave, and you wonder what happened to them.

Tape-record your team in various situations— a consultation appointment, making a financial arrangement, delivering hygiene instructions, giving post-operative instructions, etc. Replay the tape as a team. Try to determine which words might "throw off" a patient. Change those words or phrases to be more user friendly.

You might even consider playing your tapes for a non-dental person. Let them tell you what makes no sense or what is confusing. This effort could prove to be extremely valuable.

Step 2—Use a variety of teaching/ communication methods

Because people learn in a variety of ways and have different personality styles, you may want to approach your communication efforts in multiple ways. We will discuss this in further detail in Chapter 10.

KEYPOINT:

Know that just because a person says they understand doesn't mean that they do.

For example: If you are presenting a treatment plan, you may want to use before and after photographs to back up your verbal presentation. Or, you may find that certain people want only the facts while others may want a great deal of detail (refer to Chapter 4). You must be perceptive to the different behavioral styles and respond appropriately.

Step 3—Benefit statement

Make a statement reflecting the benefits of the information you have just shared.

"Mrs. Jones, you seem to be clear about the recommendations I am making. I feel this treatment will make it possible for us to save your teeth. This will prevent the need for more extensive treatment in the future."

Step 4—Close your benefit statement with a question

Why do you need to close your benefit statement with a question? To accomplish the following:

- involve the patient
- verify that you were clearly understood
- find out if questions or concerns still exist

"Mrs. Jones, do you have any questions about the treatment I am recommending?"

"If there are no further questions, is there any reason why we shouldn't schedule an appointment to begin your treatment?"

Step 5—Notice the body language

Pay attention to how the receiver of your message is responding. Are they making eye contact with you? Are they fidgeting? Do they seem preoccupied?

Remember to ask for feedback. Are you coming across well? If the person does not seem to be in touch with you, gently acknowledge this:

"You seem to be preoccupied. Is there something on your mind?"

"This doesn't seem to be a good time for you. Would you like to postpone this conversation?"

There is no reason to proceed or think you are going to be heard if you do not have the other person's attention. The human mind can only think of one thing at a time. Take a few moments to get the person's attention, then proceed or reschedule the conversation or consultation.

Step 6—Ask for feedback

The only way you will know if you are getting your message across accurately is to ask for feedback. In order to make sure your message was clear, ask questions like the following:

"Does that make sense?"

"Do you have anything to add to this?"

"How do you feel about that?"

"Did I say that clearly, or do you need more information?"

Step 7—Give positive reinforcement

Thank the person for his/her concern and attention. Let them know that you appreciate their participation with you. Again, express the value of the information you are sharing. Reinforce the benefits of your recommendations. Repetition is okay! Repetition is essential to learning.

The goal of effective speaking skills is to open the doors of communication rather than to close them. You want your messages to come across in a way that people will listen and understand. Making sure you are understood and accepted is no easy task. Just talking or lecturing will not get the results you want. Learn how to speak so others will listen.

Remember: "It's not what you say, it's how you say it!" Great communication leads to great relationships and great production.

KEYPOINT:

If someone's behavior
is having a concrete,
negative affect on you,
your performance,
or on the practice,
then you not only have
the right but also the
responsibility to address
the issue.

Addressing Challenging Issues

In Chapter 5, you learned how to listen so you can be clear about what other people are telling you. You learned the skills of listening so you can be more helpful and more effective in your relationships with team members and patients. Listening is the communicative skill to use when someone comes to you with a problem or a concern. You validate them at the same time that you are gathering necessary information so you can help them with a solution.

So far, in this chapter, you have learned speaking skills to deliver your message more clearly when you are presenting. However, you may now be asking yourself: "Great! I know what to do to help others if they have a problem. I know how to speak effectively in a presentation. But what do I do when I have a problem with someone, and I want to get my message across, or I need to let a person know that I have a problem? Are my speaking skills important in that type of situation?"

The answer is undeniably, "yes!"

It's imperative that you address the behavior and not the person. Some people have a difficult time hearing about their own performance. They take constructive criticism personally and become offended by the confrontation. Therefore, learning to speak in a non-threatening manner will move you closer to the goal of confronting constructively rather than harmfully.

You need and deserve to have your needs met. In order to be successful in getting your needs met, certain speaking skills are necessary and beneficial. Developing excellent speaking skills will accomplish the following goals:

- Get your message across accurately
- Have your needs understood and met

• Move your relationships to the next level to gain a person's trust and confidence

The specific communication skill to use when someone is causing you a problem is an "I" message, as developed by Dr. Thomas Gordon. In his book, *Leader Effectiveness Training,* Dr. Gordon suggests that when you own a problem, you should use assertiveness skills. With assertiveness skills, you will convey your needs and work toward getting those needs met, and at the same time, you will do everything possible to help the other person get their needs met. Both parties will win.

Not confronting a person whose behavior is causing you a problem doesn't serve either party well. If a person doesn't know that what they are doing is unacceptable, they can't change. If you do not confront difficult behavior, you run the risk of harming and even losing the relationship.

People become uncomfortable with confrontation because they may have received negative reactions in the past. If you have had less than great confrontational/experiences, it may be because you didn't have the necessary skills. Most people haven't ever learned how to confront in a helpful way. Let's begin that learning process.

It takes a great deal of courage to confront another person about their behavior. There is risk involved. You have to decide whether or not the person's behavior is having a concrete, negative effect on you. If it is, then the risk of confrontation becomes necessary. If the answer to that question is "no," then let it go! That may be one of the most difficult things you ever do—let go of something that may be bugging you, but is not truly a problem. In the one situation where you choose to risk confrontation, your goal will be resolution, and the skills you use will be critical to your success. In the other situation, where you choose to let go because you have determined that this person's behavior is not really causing you a problem, great stress relief may result. Do you carry around burdens, worries, upsets, and discomforts for no concrete reason? Do yourself a favor, and let them go.

"I Messages"

There are four different kinds of "I" messages. Each one is appropriate for a different situation. The goals of "I" messages are sending your messages clearly so you get your point across without hurting the other person and sending your message so your needs are made clear. "I" messages describe your thoughts, feelings, and experiences. They are not an evaluation or judgment about the other person.

4 kinds of "I" messages

- Declarative
- Responsive
- Preventive
- Confrontive

Declarative "I" messages. These messages tell other people something about you. You explain how you feel, what you are thinking, or your opinion. For example: You say to your co-workers: "I like going to lunch as a team," or "I enjoyed the course this past week." Or, you say to a patient: "I appreciate your promptness," or "I love your new smile."

Responsive "I" messages. These messages let you tell a person yes or no to something they request of you. For example: You say to a co-worker: "No, I don't want to go to lunch today. I have some work I need to catch up on during that time. But, thanks anyway," or "Yes, I can help you with your perio-charting on Mrs. Jones today." Or, you say to a patient: "No, Mrs. Jones, the doctor cannot see you at 5:00 today. He will be gone by that time," or "No, we cannot carry your account on our own books. However, we do have a financial partner who can help you."

Preventive "I" messages. These messages tell other people that you need something, and you hope to get their cooperation. The term "preventive" means that your goal is to prevent future problems, misunderstandings, or disappointments.

For example: You say to your doctor: "I would like to be able to schedule another day of hygiene with your practice. We are booked so far out with patients that we can't see them soon enough. We can't schedule people when they call because there are no openings. Plus, I need the additional income. It seems like we could both benefit from an extra day of hygiene." Or, you say to a patient: "I need you to work with me on the scheduling of these appointments. We are going to reserve two hours of Dr. Jameson's time for you at both of these appointments. We need to find a time that works for you so that we can count on you to be here."

Confrontive "I" messages. These messages tell another person that something they are doing is unacceptable to you. Something is happening that is having a concrete, negative effect on you, your performance, or the practice.

It is a message made up of three specific parts:

- The sincere emotion you are feeling
- A brief description of the behavior you find unacceptable
- The concrete, negative effect or result of that behavior

The three parts of an "I" message are as follows:

1. I feel _____(sincere emotion)

2. when_____(unacceptable behavior)

3. because_____(concrete, negative effect)

For example: A new patient is present in the office today for her initial evaluation. You have done your first overview and performed periodontal probing to determine the status of her gum tissue. Upon probing, you find evidence of pocketing and possible bone loss, so you prescribe a full mouth series of radiographs. She becomes belligerent and says she wants you to "fix her up" but she does not want "all those x-rays."

First of all, you must ask yourself the critical question, "Is what this person doing having a concrete, negative effect on me, on my performance, or on the practice?" I think you will agree that it is. Therefore, you not only have the right but also the responsibility to confront the issue.

For example: an appropriate "I" message might be "Ms. Patient, I understand your concern. However, I feel very frustrated and helpless when I cannot obtain the necessary radiographs, because without this diagnostic information I am not able to analyze your needs appropriately and will then be unable to recommend the therapy or treatment that will best meet your needs."

With this type of careful communication, your particular problem is expressed in a non-threatening, non-judgmental manner. More than likely the patient will not become angry, but will see your side of the situation and realize that you are looking out for her best interest. In essence, you have stated your "I" message in terms that will meet both of your needs.

The opposite of an "I" message is a "you" message, or a "put-down" message. A "you" message is filled with blame, judgment, and intimidation.

For example: "YOU will not be able to receive good care because YOU are refusing the x-rays. YOU make it impossible for us to do what we need to do."

Most of us are great at sending "you" messages. "You" messages are usually ineffective in getting a person to change their behavior. A person will often become defensive or antagonistic, because they have been "slam dunked," and their interest in helping you is diminished. When a person becomes defensive, effective communication stops.

Practice and use all of the types of "I" messages. They will help you assertively get your needs met in a constructive manner. They will help you in handling difficult situations, whether with team members or with patients. All of you will become better leaders and will be more productive if you learn to determine whether you have a problem or not, and if so, who "owns" the problem. Determine how you can confront the problem without harming the integrity of the other person.

IN SUMMARY

Speaking is a part of the two-way communication flow. Presenting yourself and your message clearly is beneficial to both relationships and to your presentation success.

Do everything you can to develop and maintain good relationships. However, sometimes things get difficult. Sometimes people and relationships become difficult. What then? How do you handle difficult people and situations?

CHAPTER 55

HANDLING DIFFICULT PEOPLE AND DIFFICULT SITUATIONS

Nobody can make you feel inferior without your consent.

— ELEANOR ROOSEVELT

*H*ave you ever had, or do you presently have, any difficult patients in your practice?

- Is there someone who is difficult to understand or with whom you have difficulty relating?
- Do some of your patients make mountains out of molehills at every visit?
- Are some of your patients troublemakers? Stubborn? Hostile?
- Do some of your patients have special needs that make treatment difficult?

If you answered "yes" to any of the preceding questions, then you probably maintain a normal flow of patients in your practice—patients who range from one extreme to the other.

Webster defines difficult as "hard to understand or reach, painful, laborious, troublesome, puzzling, exacting, and stubborn."

We all know difficult patients and must deal with them. Learning to deal with them effectively can turn potentially negative situations into positive ones. Excellent and effective communication in these situations can not only prevent a patient from leaving your practice and "bad mouthing" you across town, but it can also turn a somewhat loyal patient into a "forever" patient who becomes an ambassador for your practice.

Business experts tell us that identifying a difficult person or situation and taking action to give special care to that person or to correct the situation can be beneficial for the further development of your company—in your case, your dental practice.

Let's look at difficult situations or patients. Having the appropriate armamentarium will have a positive and long lasting effect on your production, your enjoyment of dentistry, and your stress control.

Differences that May Lead to Conflict or Rejection

Remembering Chapter 4 , know that when a patient is difficult or your relationship with a patient becomes difficult, that is no indication either party is right or wrong, it may just indicate that differences exist. However, these differences can cause conflict and be tough to handle.

Differences that can lead to conflict or rejection usually stem from:

- a misunderstanding or lack of appreciation for variances in personality
- an incompatibility of goals

A misunderstanding or lack of appreciation for personality differences

Many problems can be overcome if a study and an acceptance of the variances between and among people are pursued. Just because a person is different from you or doesn't feel the same way as you doesn't mean that either of you is right or wrong. It simply means that you have divergent opinions or you are unclear about each other's goals. This lack of understanding can lead to difficulties or to fear.

Difficult behavior, including defensiveness, is often a result of fear. Being a receptive listener, letting a person get their emotions out on the table, encouraging a person to say what he/she wants, and understanding the person without condemning ideas and opinions can relieve tension and reduce or eliminate fear.

Being a good listener and communicator and being willing to hear a person allows you to show respect to the person. Encouraging the expression of opinion without judgment will often lead to a quieter, more receptive patient—one who may become a faithful friend of the practice.

Let's review the four personality styles:

- Choleric—the driving personality that wants results and control
- Sanguine—the enthusiastic personality that wants attention and positive strokes
- Melancholy—the congenial personality that wants compatibility and harmony
- Phlegmatic—the steady personality that wants structure and organization

Identifying these temperaments lets you know that each of your patients is unique and treating each of them in exactly the same manner or presenting your recommendations in the same way is inappropriate and ineffective.

Incompatibility of goals. Incompatibility of goals can also be a source of conflict. The goals you might want to accomplish may differ from the goals of the patient. On the other hand, you and a patient might want the same goal of excellent oral health, but your individual plans of action for accomplishing that goal might be incompatible. Even when conflict begins with a rational disagreement about the goal or about the action plan, emotions might erupt and stifle an agreeable solution.

Have you ever had a patient in the office and no matter what you did, it was always wrong? Did you feel the harder you tried, the deeper you dug yourself into a hole?

This failure to communicate is often the explanation for conflict or for unfulfilled relationships. Effective communication may not resolve all conflicts. It may not bring two people with totally different goals to a place of commonality, but utilization of these skills can do the following:

- enhance your ability to influence a person's acceptance of your recommendations
- smooth the actual treatment experience
- persuade a person to carry out necessary follow-up therapies

ACTIVE LISTENING AS A CALMING AGENT

You have already learned the single most effective skill you can use to calm an irate person, defuse anger, handle a difficult person, or on the other hand, to further enhance a good relationship—active listening. Listening is a skill that can be developed through conscious effort, and it can be improved through practice.

In review, active listening is reflecting back to the person what you think you have heard him/her saying to make sure that you have heard correctly. A simple repetition or paraphrasing is not sufficient. The listener should demonstrate in his/her own words an adequate understanding of the content, intent, and emotion of the speaker's remarks.

This type of listening gives you the opportunity to clarify and ensure that you understand what the patient is trying to say. It also has a definite calming effect by providing feedback and maintaining a supportive atmosphere.

DEALING WITH CONFLICT CONSTRUCTIVELY

We sometimes think it is not okay to disagree with another person— certainly not a patient. We think they will not like us if we express our own thoughts or feelings. Therefore, we keep our thoughts to ourselves. Sometimes, if left inside to dwell, these differences of opinion grow from a simple disagreement to a major alienation, and even a loss of clients.

Positive disagreement

You can disagree with a patient in a positive manner that can prevent difficulties from developing. To disagree positively, follow these steps:

- Actively listen to make sure you are hearing the person accurately

- Let the person know that you understand or appreciate his/her viewpoint
- Express your own opinion

For example:

Patient: "I understand your financial policy, but I just want to pay this out."

Business Administrator: "You would rather take several months to take care of your financial responsibility, is that right?"

Patient: "Yes, I can only pay $50 per month. I can't pay all of this next week!"

Business Administrator: "I can appreciate that, Ms. Patient, but we do not carry long term accounts on our books. If you need long term, convenient financing, we offer several alternative payment options. Let's discuss these."

Constructive confrontation

Do you avoid confrontation at all cost? Are you nervous about confronting another person because you might hurt their feelings, make them angry, or cause greater conflict?

Positive disagreement does not always take you far enough in the confrontation modality. You sometimes need to go further. Facing an issue "head on" is the best and most constructive way in which to deal with a conflict or with problem behavior. Tucking the conflict away may create anxiety, anger, and negativity on the part of both parties. If you decide the relationship is worth developing, or in some cases saving, then the risk of confrontation may prove to be a gift you give to yourself, to the other party, and to the relationship. Lashing out or putting another person down is totally non-productive. Differences handled in this manner are often unresolvable.

So how do you confront constructively? How do you let a person know that you do not approve of their behavior without hurting them? How do you preserve the sanctity of the relationship and let a person know that you aren't pleased about something?

The characteristics of constructive confrontation are as follows:

- Actively listen to make sure that the feelings and the issue are clearly understood
- Let the person know that you appreciate their viewpoint or situation
- Confront him/her with specific changes that must occur. Stick to concrete, tangible issues such as time, money, responsibility, etc.

For example: You are the appointment coordinator. You have reserved two long appointments for extensive crown and bridge treatment for Ms. Patient. She rescheduled the first appointment, and she simply did not show up for the second one even though you had confirmed the appointment the day before. Now she is calling to reschedule.

Appointment Coordinator: "Ms. Patient, it seems that keeping your appointments has been a problem for you. I understand you have a very busy schedule. However, Ms. Patient, unless we can have a commitment from you that you will be at the next scheduled appointment, I am afraid I will be unable to reserve any further time for you. We care very much about you and about providing your treatment, but we need to ask that you respect our time so we can provide all of our patients with our best attention."

Notice the three parts of the confrontation. The appointment coordinator:

- summarized the person's behavior and fed that back to her
- informed her that she understood the challenges of her busy schedule
- confronted her, diplomatically, about the needed change in behavior

The goal of the appointment coordinator was not to hurt the patient, embarrass her, or turn her away from the practice. Her goal was to address the behavior that was causing problems for her and the whole team. She had the right and the responsibility to address this issue. Addressing it in such a way that the patient understood how her behavior was adversely affecting many other people would hopefully encourage her to change that behavior. Allowing her to continue scheduling appointments and conveniently breaking them was not doing her or the practice any good.

You may be saying, "We don't need her anyway. If she doesn't respect us enough to keep her appointments, then we just need to let her go and fill her place with a patient who is more respectful." Perhaps. However, I would encourage you to try to deal constructively with problems. Know that successful people are not people who don't have problems. They are people who have learned how to successfully solve their problems.

Either/or confrontation

When extreme measures have been attempted to restore a situation or to encourage a change in behavior, but the necessary alteration has not occurred, either/or confrontation is appropriate. Either/or confrontation gives a final solution offer—an ultimatum. It is a last opportunity to make required changes. This is an extreme measure and should be used only in situations where an either/or situation exists.

The characteristics of either/or confrontation are as follows:

- Deliver a confrontive "I" message
- Stick to the facts that are observable. Don't assume
- Stay in the future tense. What will happen in the future if compliance to the required change does not occur? What are the consequences of non-compliance?
- Don't bring up issues from the past
- If the person tries to justify their behavior—ignore the efforts. Do not accept "yeah, buts!"

Remember: you have probably confronted this person and this issue in several, *gentler* ways. Non-compliance to your previous efforts to resolve the conflict has led to this moment. Ultimately, the person is choosing this firm and powerful method of confrontation. At this point, you have little or no choice.

For example: You have carefully made a financial arrangement with a patient. She has signed the financial agreement form and has indicated that the chosen method of payment is acceptable. However, the patient has been consistently late with payment and has now missed a payment. You have sent letters notifying her of the past due status of her account, and you have made collection calls to her. Now, 90 days have passed since her last payment.

Financial Coordinator: "Ms. Patient, I am concerned about the fact that we have not received a payment from you in the past 90 days. I have spoken with you and corresponded with you several times over the last 3 months. You have indicated that we can expect your payment, and yet those payments have not been received. Now, Ms. Patient, I must tell you that if we do not receive full payment within 10 days of this notification, we will be forced to turn your account over for legal action.

If we turn over your account, this will have a negative effect on your credit for several years. We want to work this out with you, but have not received your cooperation. It will be beneficial to you to resolve this problem now and avoid future credit problems."

This is a strong measure (a strong method) of confrontation. Perhaps you will never need this type of confrontation knowledge. But if you do, this is a proven method of handling difficult situations and people in an acceptable manner.

Conflict resolution

The process of resolving a conflict with a difficult patient is a complex process with consequences that endure beyond the event itself. Conflict is inevitable. Thus, an understanding of and a competence in the skills of effective communication and conflict resolution are critical.

ASK YOURSELF THESE QUESTIONS

- Understanding the level of difficulty, is it worth the effort to deal with the person?
- Are you willing and able to find out what this person's particular needs might be?
- Can you meet those needs?
- Are you beating your head against the wall?
- If the conflict is not resolved, and you do not come to equitable terms for both parties, do you want to maintain the relationship?

Ask yourself these questions. Answer them honestly. Handle the difficult patients and situations to the best of your ability. Know that it will take an incredible amount of effort and energy. The difficult person may not realize your efforts; they may not appreciate your efforts at all. It has been said that 5% of the people give you 95% of the problems. That's probably true. However, that 5% is stressful with a capital "S!"

PROBLEM-SOLVING

As I said before, successful people (or successful dental practices) are not free of problems. Everyone has problems. However, the successful ones have learned to identify and overcome them. Therein lies the difference.

In my doctoral work on the effect of communicative skill training on the control of stress, I surveyed 3,000 practices. Every position in the practice was represented in the surveys. Interestingly, when asked if the practice had a problem-solving system in place, not one practice or person answered affirmatively.

I want you to be among the successful—ultimately successful—both personally and professionally. Let's put all of these communication skills together and develop a problem-solving system for you and your practice.

What follows are the seven steps to successful problem-solving.

Define the problem

Determine what is happening that is unacceptable. Identify the problem in terms of what each party needs. It is imperative as you are working on the solving of your problem that you make sure the needs of each party are met. Otherwise, your efforts will be useless. If a person's needs are not met by the solution, he/she will, unlikely, abide by the solution.

This step of problem-solving may take longer than any of the other steps. That's fine. Take as long as you need. Be sure not to jump off into developing solutions until clarity of needs has been established. Use both the "I" messages and active listening skills here.

Brainstorm possible solutions

During this phase of problem-solving—get creative. Throw out as many ideas as possible to solve the problem. Do not analyze the ideas at this point. Brainstorm. Write down the ideas that are suggested. Don't give any opinions—affirmatively or negatively. Set your minds on "free flow" and generate possible solutions. Again, do not be critical of anyone for a particular idea—that's a sure way to shut down the brainstorming process.

Discuss each possible solution

Once all ideas have been presented, it is time to discuss the pros and the cons of each one. Be respectful of the other person's ideas. You may not like the idea, and you may not agree with it. However, use your positive disagreement skills here. Respect the other person's right to have their own opinion. Disagree in a diplomatic manner.

Come to a consensus agreement

Together, determine the solution or solutions that you believe will work best for you. If a possible solution has too many cons, you'd better eliminate that one or approach it from a different perspective. If there are too many cons, it simply will not work over time.

Design a plan of action

Go back to the five-step goal accomplish process outlined in Chapter 2. Using this process, design a plan of action as to how you will make the solving of your problem a reality. In review:

Write the goal—the problem you want to solve. Write it in the affirmative. Express your intention.

Design the plan of action—the things you must do. What will you do, how will you do it, and why is a particular task important. Identify any resources you might need and identify barriers so you can work through them.

Person or persons responsible. Assign the responsibilities of each task to the appropriate person. Make sure that each person is clear about what he/she is supposed to do and is ready to accept the responsibility.

Time frame. Establish the time frame for the completion of each task.

Evaluate. Schedule a time to get back together to see how things are going.

Put the plan into action

You have made great effort to solve your problem. Obviously, you care about each other and your relationship or you wouldn't have worked this hard. Now, you've designed a plan of action. Commit to putting the plan into action and carrying out the responsibilities you have agreed upon.

Evaluate

Determine if your plan of action is working. If things are working well, pat each other on the back. If things are not working well, step back to the brainstorming phase of the problem-solving and start again. It will be worth it. Go back to your definition of needs. Make sure the needs of each party are being met. You want to create a WIN-WIN situation. Both parties need to "win" in order for your problem-solving to be considered successful.

Things to avoid while problem-solving:

- Don't be critical of each other's ideas
- Don't leave out any of the seven steps
- Don't disappoint your teammate by not following through with your agreement
- Don't forget to use the good communication skills that are foundational to the success of problem-solving

There you have it—seven steps of problem-solving. This is a proven method that can be used when a problem is large or small. It can be used with team members or with patients. It can be used if there are only two people involved or if the entire team is involved.

You may be asking, "How does problem-solving impact great production?" Let me suggest several ways:

- Problems that are left unsolved sap the energy from team members and from their individual productivity, which will obviously impact the ultimate productivity of the practice

- Team members who feel their needs are heard and that efforts are made to meet these needs are more connected to the practice. Their commitment translates to improved performance

- If a problem exists with one of your systems, management or clinical, that "glitch" in the system will have a negative impact on all other systems. The systems of your practice are so intricately connected that every single system must be carefully developed and beautifully administered

- If you have a collection problem with your patients, this problem-solving system is effective

- Scheduling challenges can be worked on by following this system

- In addition, if you think about it, by following these seven steps with a patient as you are determining the patient's needs and wants and a plan of action for meeting those needs and wants, you are really problem-solving. The seven-step process can be applied to case planning, presentation, delivery, and follow-up

DO WE CREATE OUR OWN DIFFICULT PATIENTS?

I once spoke with a 37-year-old doctor who was in his 11th year of practice. He was calling to discuss our consulting services. His practice was not doing well, and he was extremely frustrated.

During that initial interview, some obvious barriers to the success of his practice emerged:

- He didn't really like doing dentistry!

- He was in financial woe
- He said he had no management systems in place—he had no systems at all!
- He resented his patients. He felt he was performing a well-rehearsed play every day because he really didn't like what he was doing and didn't even want to see those patients. He said dentistry was only a means to an end—MONEY (of which he had none)
- He was attracting very few new patients to the practice and was concerned that the end was near
- He was a graduate of one of the most respected post-graduate clinical institutes, but he felt he had been misled by all of the "gurus" who believed that commitment to quality could and would lead to personal, professional, and financial fulfillment. So he was angry
- He felt that everyone was out to get him
- He said his greatest frustration came when people wanted the quality, long lasting, proven service but were angry with him for the fee

REFLECTION: THE MIRROR EFFECT

Don't our patients reflect us? The conversation with this frustrated doctor validated an underlying philosophy of my management—patients are a mirror of you and of your practice. If you don't like how your patients respond to you or to your recommendations, put a mirror in front of all aspects of your practice, from telephone to greeting to presentation to financial arrangements to treatment to follow-up, etc. What are you putting out there? Whatever you are putting out there will come right back to you.

MOTIVATION

The researcher Frederick Herzberg studied motivators that deal with the issues of job satisfaction and fulfillment found in the workplace. The following factors, in order of strength, characterize the highly motivated individual:

- Achievement
- Recognition

- The work itself
- Responsibility
- Advancement
- Personal and professional fulfillment

Let's see how the presence or the absence of these factors may have negatively affected this young doctor.

Achievement

This doctor wanted to achieve clinical expertise. He had attended the best clinical courses available and numerous management courses as well. However, the achievement of this goal (clinical excellence) had been stifled by his inability to attract people to his practice and by his inability to gain acceptance of treatment recommendations.

He wanted to achieve financial security, but this goal had not been accomplished, because a healthy new patient flow and case acceptance had not been achieved. One ties directly into the other.

The cycle had become a vicious one. The fewer the number of new patients, the fewer cases presented. The fewer cases presented, the fewer cases accepted. The fewer the cases accepted, the lower the revenues for the practice. The lower the revenues for the practice, the more discouraged he became. The more discouraged he became, the fewer the new patients, etc. This had become a vicious cycle for him. What you put out there in all things, including attitude, comes back to you.

Recognition

Recognition is the number-two motivator of people in the work environment. This doctor said, "I'm over wanting to be recognized as a quality dentist or as the practice that offers 'only the best', etc. I just want to make a living. This dentistry stuff is just a job. It's just a means to an end."

Tied closely to recognition by colleagues, clients, or family is a strong sense of well-being—a strong sense of self worth. If a person doesn't feel good about him/herself; if a person doesn't believe in personal worth; if a person doesn't love him/herself, then it is impossible to love another person fully, sincerely, and unconditionally.

Perhaps here was the greatest barrier—the greatest problem—for our young doctor. This man couldn't love his patients, his staff, his practice, or dentistry. His sense of self-worth was so low that he had lost the level of caring for himself. He needed to feel good about himself before he could reach out to others. If he couldn't sincerely reach out to others, who would be attracted to the practice? If he wasn't confident in himself, how could his patients be confident in him? Without this strong level of confidence and trust, case acceptance had become an unreachable goal.

The work itself

Earl Nightengale says, "We become what we think about." The subconscious mind does not know the difference between reality and non-reality. Therefore, whatever is fed into the mind stays there—forever. All thought processes are filtered through the subconscious mind.

When this doctor constantly said to himself and to others "I don't even like dentistry," his mind acted on those thoughts. The mind goes to work to put thought into action.

Not liking the dentistry had become a self-fulfilling prophecy. The more he thought, "I don't like dentistry," the more he didn't. The more he didn't like dentistry, the fewer patients he was attracting. The fewer new patients he was attracting, the fewer cases accepted. The fewer the number of cases accepted, the lower the practice revenues, etc.

Responsibility

Human beings thrive on the entrustment of responsibility. This entrustment is a motivator. Enthusiasm for a project is generated when responsibility is given and trust is imparted.

When another person gives us the responsibility to provide a service or to carry out a specific task, we are motivated. The human being responds more effectively to positive reinforcement than to negative reinforcement. Entrustment and responsibility are perceived as just that— positive reinforcement.

This doctor was experiencing a void in his inner self because he was not being given the responsibility of caring for many patients. Most doctors tell me that the driving force for entering dentistry in the first place and (the sustaining drive for continuing in the profession) is "having the opportunity to help people achieve greater health and optimum beauty." If that responsibility is not an ongoing part of the work itself, then motivation exits and love of the work itself leaves.

Advancement

In the corporate world, the opportunity for advancement is obvious. One knows what opportunities lie ahead and where one can go in the advancement scenario.

However, in dentistry, advancement doesn't have the same black and white definition. Advancement is less obvious. Advancement for the dentist might mean:

- financial advancement—more net profit
- greater clinical proficiency
- leadership development
- team building
- addition of associates/partnerships
- etc.

This young doctor was not accomplishing any of the above. Therefore, advancement was not a motivator. In fact, the lack of advancement in each of the above listed areas was becoming a *de-motivator.*

Personal and professional fulfillment

Money is a motivator, but it will only go so far with the human being. We all know of a person who "has everything" except happiness.

Dentistry's beloved and respected mentor, L.D. Pankey, reemphasized Aristotle's Cross of Life and encouraged us to strive for a balance in our lives; a balance between work/play/love/worship.

We can and will accomplish personal and professional fulfillment in the practice of dentistry when we realize that balance gives us energy, motivation, and happiness. As simple as it may sound, happiness is what each person is really striving for, in dentistry and in life (Fig. 7-1).

The Cross of Reward from Dr. Pankey indicates another area for needed balance—knowing yourself, your patients, your work, and your own knowledge (Fig. 7-2).

What wisdom! Combine these four intricate and essential factors, starting with number one—*know yourself.* Knowing yourself—the good and the bad—is essential for growth.

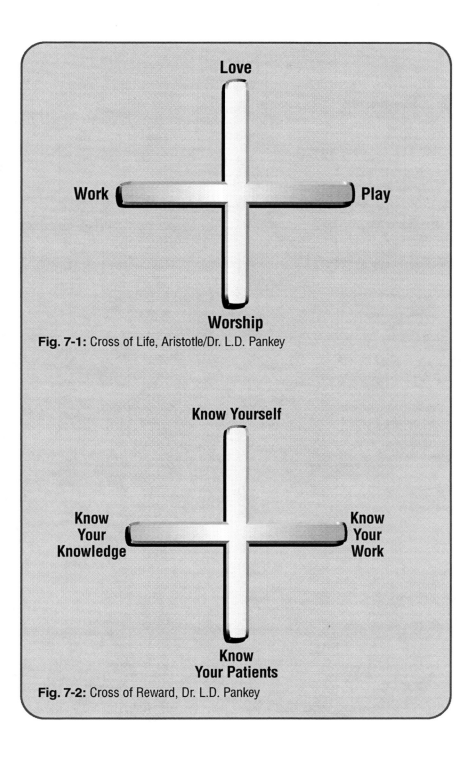

Fig. 7-1: Cross of Life, Aristotle/Dr. L.D. Pankey

Fig. 7-2: Cross of Reward, Dr. L.D. Pankey

IN SUMMARY

Put a mirror up to your practice and to yourself. Take an honest look. Find the strengths—maximize these. Find the weaknesses—work on overcoming these. The mirror effect is strong. The strength can be turned in your favor. Concentrate on the positives. Turn negatives into positives. Feed your mind the good stuff, and that's what will come your way. Remember: "you become what you think about."

Definition of your problem or weak areas is the first step toward solving the problem or overcoming the weakness.

SPECIAL PEOPLE/SPECIAL NEEDS

THE PARENT/CHILD

*P*roviding dental care for children can be an extremely enjoyable and rewarding experience. As dental professionals and dental educators, you must be aware of and use methods of building strong relationships with the children and their parents before treatment can be successful. The ability to deliver quality treatment in a non-stressful manner is dependent upon the cooperative behavior of the child.

The parent and child or both can become difficult patients when fear becomes a dominating factor in the dental experience.

Children can develop fear in one of three ways:

- By learning the fear as a direct imitation of a family member (brother, sister, or parent) or from a friend
- By associating the dental experience with an existing fear
- By actually having a painful or frightening experience

If an appointment with a child becomes uncontrolled because of fear, if the child tries his/her very best both physically and vocally to protest the impending treatment, then both the child and the dental team suffer. C. M. McElroy says, "Although the operative dentistry may be perfect, the appointment is a failure if the child departs in tears."

Experts in the area of dental behavior agree that dental attitudes usually develop in childhood. The development of a negative attitude, caused by a negative experience in childhood, can lead to dental fear and dental avoidance in adulthood. The best way to handle the difficult parent/child situation is to prevent the situation in the first place, whenever and wherever possible.

PREVENTION OF FEAR

As dental professionals, you are committed to prevention—clinically. In addition, being committed to prevention behaviorally serves both the patient and the provider. The prevention of or the constructive dealing with fear will lead to positive relationships among the parent, child, and the dental team.

What can be done to set the tone for a good parent/child situation?

Environment

A child is acutely aware of every aspect of his/her surroundings. The senses are tuned in to everything that is happening as a result of the child's innate inquisitiveness. The child's interpretation of the dental experience is affected by all of the senses—hearing, sight, smell, touch, and taste.

Hearing

- Noises made by the dental equipment—suction, hand piece, etc.
- The sounds of the doctor's or the assistant's voice—quiet and smooth are relaxing, while hurried and rough can cause tension
- Words—use of positive words can set a positive tone, while use of negative words can stimulate fear or apprehension

For example:

- "make you comfortable" vs. "get you out of pain"
- "special pictures of your teeth" vs. "x-rays"

Sight

- Have a specially designed space for the children, a space in which they feel at home, in control, and comfortable

- Games, books, children's magazines, video games, small tables. All of these give the appearance and the feeling that the child is welcome in your practice. They don't feel so overwhelmed by big things!
- Smiling faces from all members of the team, including the doctor, will calm a child.
- Instruments and needles should be kept out of the sight of the child

Smell

- Try to soften any "dental" smells by using air freshener or fresh flowers (kept out of the reach of the children, of course)
- Scented candles can be burning in the business office so the soft fragrance wisps throughout the office
- Use the scented gloves or scented nitrous oxide nosepieces
- Careful attention must be paid to the grooming of the dentist and the assistants. Be sure to be pleasantly scented. Include the use of mouthwash on a regular basis throughout your day

Touch

- Touch the child with firm, but gentle touches of reassurance
- Allow the child to touch the equipment and instruments—the mirror, handpiece, and hoses.

Dr. Bill Bozalis, a graduate of the pediatric department of Northwestern University Dental School, says that he lets the child hold the mouth mirror. He also lets the child feel the gloves. (Of

KEYPOINT:

"If the child feels that they are in some control, they are more cooperative."

course, no instruments are in his hands at this time.) "We let the kids feel the gloves, the mask, etc., so that they are not intimidated or alarmed at the infection control tools. They realize that they are a normal part of the visit. Once they have had a chance to feel the tools, they seem less concerned about them."

- Shake hands with the child. This will give the child an important physical contact with you and will make him/her feel special
- Let the child hold the saliva ejector in his/her mouth. The child will love being your "helper" and will be more cooperative

Taste

- Make sure that the topical anesthesia has a flavor the child will like
- Rinse the child's mouth quickly to eliminate any unpleasant tastes
- Fluoride and toothpaste flavors must also be pleasantly flavored. You may wish to offer a variety of flavors to give the child that important sense of choice and control

Preparation

In addition to the above listed criteria in setting the tone of a positive dental experience for the child, careful preplanning of the visit will be to everyone's advantage. Dr. Eugene Litteken, a graduate of Baylor University School of Pediatric Dentistry, believes that educating the parent and the child prior to and throughout treatment is "the single most important factor for effective treatment to take place."

Dr. Litteken believes one of the most difficult situations with which he has to deal in his pediatric practice is when a parent or a child comes to the office with misinformation or with an incorrect interpretation of information.

"Parents or children may tell you one thing, but what's really happening is something totally different. What they are saying and what they are meaning may also be two different things. By asking open-ended questions that establish good lines of communication, we are able to see where the parent/child are coming from. In this manner, the parent and/or the child both feel a sense of comfort and a sense of control. They know that we are listening to them and that we want to work with them to solve their problem or to meet their needs. Then, they will be more likely to cooperate with us when we recommend treatment. That initial contact is critical."

The preparation of the parent and the child for their initial visit is essential for a cooperative new patient experience and for a long-term relationship. Much effort has been placed on figuring out what type of initial experience will be most likely to reduce anxiety.

The dental team needs to take the time and put forth the effort to educate the parent in advance of the appointment. This will reduce the risk of the parent negatively preparing the child. Children who are well prepared for their visit tend to be more cooperative than those children who are inappropriately prepared.

Parents who themselves are not dentally literate or who have had a negative experience often provide a poor preparation for their children. Parents who do not really know what a dentist does or how he/she does it will often mislead a child—sometimes in a harmful way.

For example: A parent who thinks a dentist is someone who pulls teeth will not likely prepare a child for a happy visit. When a child goes into an appointment thinking something is wrong, they are less cooperative. However, when going into the appointment thinking that the dentist is someone who takes good care of you and of your teeth, the child is more relaxed and cooperative.

The pre-appointment letter

The pre-appointment letter has been recommended for several decades as an effective manner in which the dentist can help the parent to properly prepare the child for their initial visit. Research has supported the concept that such an educational piece, when sent prior to the initial visit, will do the following:

KEYPOINT:

How the parent prepares their child for the first visit to the dentist will set the tone for that visit.

- Help the parents to be better prepared
- Encourage the child's cooperative behavior
- Reduce broken appointments

This educational letter does not need to be long or complicated. It should serve as a welcome to the parent and child and should provide a brief description of the initial visit. It should give the parent some suggestions about how they can prepare their child for this visit including some verbal skills for describing the dentist and the visit (Fig. 8-1).

Dear // (parent's name)//,

Welcome to our dental practice! All of us on the team look forward to meeting you and your child/children. We are going to take good care of both of you.

We wanted to let you know what will be happening on your first visit. This information will help both of you to feel more at home and more comfortable with us.

We want to help your child be an excellent dental patient who will be able to accept routine dental care. Preparing the child at home prior to the initial visit is very important. The following are some suggestions to guide you as you prepare your child:

1. Your child's dental visits are going to be a normal part of growing up. Please do not give your child the idea that there is anything to fear. There isn't.

2. Don't make a big deal out of the visit. It is best to tell your child the day of the appointment.

3. If your child should ask questions, explain that the dentist will look at his teeth to make sure they are healthy.

4. Please do not threaten the child with a visit to the dentist—for anything: misbehavior, not brushing, eating the wrong thing, etc.

We are enclosing a medical history and a patient information sheet for you to complete and mail back to our office in advance of your visit. Filling this out at home will let you do so at your own pace and will allow us to see your child more quickly upon arrival. We have included a self-addressed, stamped envelope for your convenience.

During your child's first visit, the following things will happen:

1. We will review the child's health history with you.
2. We will spend time with the child to get acquainted and to assess his/her emotional development.
3. We will try to build a comfortable relationship with your child by asking questions so that he/she is involved with the appointment. We want to know your child better, and we want him/her to know us better.
4. We will discuss any areas of concern with you.
5. We take a look at the child while he is sitting up to assess dental conditions.
6. We take special pictures of the child's teeth.
7. We keep this first visit very low key and always tell the child what we are going to do before we do it. We tell the child what is going to be done. Next, we show him/her what is going to be done. Then we do it.
8. We will always tell your child when even the slightest thing goes well. We want to positively reinforce your child to establish his/her good behavior.
9. Then, we schedule an appointment for a cleaning.
10. If further treatment is necessary, we will discuss this fully with you prior to the making of an appointment. There will be no treatment provided until we have built a

strong relationship. This will be important for your child's continued comfort as a dental patient.

Our practice is committed to prevention and to total health. By starting your child early in life, we can prevent decay and dental disease with early detection, oral hygiene care, and diet counseling.

Your child, with your help and cooperation, can become and remain a good dental patient with a healthy mouth and a happy smile.

We look forward to meeting you.

Sincerely,

Dr // // and Team

Fig. 8-1: Pre-appointment Letter

In addition to the letter sent to the parents prior to the visit, it is recommended that the child receive a card or note addressed specifically to him/her (Fig. 8-2). Children, for the most part, don't receive much mail, but they are usually thrilled when they do.

The initial visit

The initial visit should consist of the steps listed in your pre-appointment letter. Children, like adults, fear the unknown, and on the other hand, gain comfort and security from knowing what to expect. Therefore:

- Use simple, straightforward language when addressing the child. Explain what you are going to do prior to each procedure

- Demonstrate the procedure on yourself or on an inanimate object
- When you are confident that the child understands what is going to be done, then proceed

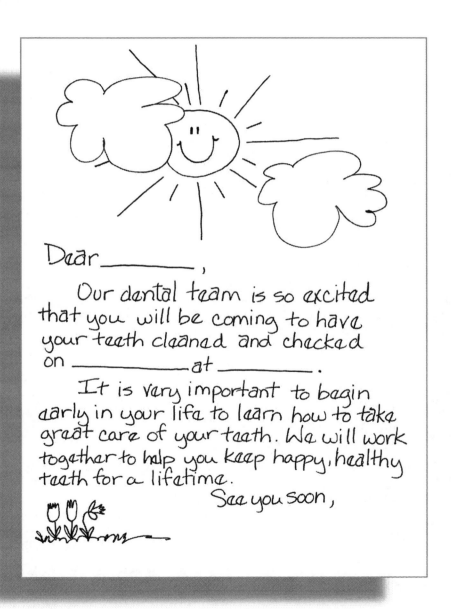

Fig. 8-2: Children's Letter
by Dru Halverson, RDH, Director of Consulting, Jameson Management, Inc.

As important as the tell, show, do method has proven to be throughout the years, nothing seems to be more significant in helping to assure a positive dental visit for a child than friendly interaction with the dental personnel outside of the operatory environment. Research has shown this type of positive interaction outweighs any other type of preparatory efforts or explanations.

Everyone on the team must realize how significant his/her interaction with the child may be! Time spent with one of the dental auxiliary in a neutral area of the office seems to be one of the strongest criteria for a calm, relaxed, confident appointment for the child.

LEARNING MODELS

Modeling

Permitting a child to watch other children or to watch Mom or Dad undergo dental treatment has been recommended as a method of preparing a child for the initial dental experience. This method of learning states that the child learns by watching. Show the child what will happen and how they are expected to behave. Children do not know what is expected of them in the dental environment, and even though you can explain the required behavior, nothing is more effective than for them to actually see what is expected of them.

Modeling is one of the most accepted and proven methods of eliciting calm, cooperative behavior in the child, especially the dentally inexperienced child. If a cooperative sibling is available for demonstration, the neophyte child should be given the opportunity to observe this sibling undergoing treatment. If a sibling or a parent is not available, another cooperative child can be observed. (Of course, you will want to make sure that the chosen child or model is cooperative.)

Distraction

The length of time the child is asked to sit in the chair for treatment depends on the child's ability to remain immobile. It is normal for a child to have a short attention span and a short span of time in which they can sit still. Vary the length of time for the appointments according to the child's own physical and emotional abilities.

If you are performing longer appointments, distraction may be to your advantage. Videotapes, mounted TV monitors, or virtual reality headsets can provide such distraction. Headsets with music or stories can also prove to be a valid distraction. The appointment will fly by for the child, and the child will be more cooperative if thinking of something besides what you are doing.

Reward and punishment

Consequences following a specific behavior play an important role in learning. It is important to understand the effects of both positive and negative reinforcement.

It is important never to punish a child in the dental environment. Physical punishment has no place in the dental arena. Mild punishment is usually ineffective in the first place, and punishment can lead to a lifetime of dental phobia.

Albert Bandura states in his research on this subject that "The resulting avoidant responses may be more socially undesirable than the behavior the punishment was originally intended to reduce, and once established, these behaviors may be considerably more difficult to eliminate."

Punishment must be administered early in a sequence of behaviors to be effective. The administration must be consistent. If a child is not punished until a full-blown tantrum has occurred, then the effectiveness of the punishment is greatly reduced.

Research on the use of punishment has shown that more often than not, punishment has the opposite effect of what is desired. It usually increases uncooperative behavior, and may increase the tantrum and aggressive behavior. Efforts to control a child's behavior with verbal or physical force result in a child who is resistant and uncooperative.

On the other hand, when the dentist gives simple instructions to the child as to what is expected of him, shows the child what should be done, then gives the child feedback on his performance—cooperation usually follows. An "instruction only" method of learning solidifies cooperative behavior far better than a punishment method. Punishment is not acceptable.

Communication

Dr. Litteken believes that "It is absolutely essential that we establish open lines of communication with the child if we are to be successful with future care." In order to establish those open lines of communication, Dr. Litteken says, "We educate our parents and our children about our standard of care. If they tell us it has been done differently in another office, we tell them that we understand this, but in our office we do it this way. Then we explain why in terms of how the difference will be beneficial to the child.

We find out what the problem is and then design a plan of action for the child. We try to keep the parent involved with the design of the plan of treatment. We do this by asking open-ended questions of the parent. This makes them feel comfortable and gives the parent a sense of control. When the parent is given the option of making choices, they sense control, even though the doctor is actually in control."

Assuming this type of respectful communication modality with the parent is critical. It is also critical that the entire team address the child with the same type of respect.

Sometimes people change the way they speak when they are with a child. Artificial speech, a high-pitched tone of voice, a singsong rhythm of speech, or "ooey gooey" language is inappropriate. Likewise, speaking slowly and specifically as if this would allow the child to understand more clearly is also an inappropriate method of communication. Children will respond most effectively when you use the same tone of voice with which you address your adult patients.

Dr. Norm Olson, the former Dean of Northwestern University School of Dentistry, encourages the dentist and the entire dental team to "treat the children like adults and the adults like children."

Food for thought, wouldn't you agree?

Vocabulary

In terms of vocabulary, a child, depending on the age, will have certain limitations of understanding. Be sure to address your education and your explanations of treatment in terminology that is concrete rather than abstract—present tense rather than future tense—relevant to the child rather than relevant to another. If you make a promise, keep it. If you tell a child something, mean it. If you ask something of a child, follow up on your request.

Be honest and open with your children patients. Let them know what you are going to do before you do it. Let them know what you expect of them. Inform them of the expected mode of behavior. Give the child positive feedback throughout the procedure.

SPECIAL BEHAVIORAL CHALLENGES WITH CHILDREN

The shy child

Do not force yourself on the shy child. Do not try to tease the child into being more responsive. This will usually produce the opposite of what you want. This effort to bring the child out will usually drive him/her deeper into Mommy's arms. Focus your attention and your comments on the parent. Then, from time to time, look at the child and give him/her a wink, but make no verbal contact with the child at this point. At first the child will withdraw, but sooner or later will be looking toward you anticipating the wink and the attention. Before long, you will be able to draw the child out by asking questions and by getting him/her involved in the conversation.

Avoid teasing a child about a state of anxiety. Doing this will only prove to the child that (just as he thought) it is not okay to be afraid. Telling a

KEYPOINT:

Speaking in a normal tone of voice with normal inflections is more effective than talking down to the child.

person it is not okay to be afraid will do nothing to defuse that fear. Rather, acknowledging the fear and letting the child know you understand his/her feelings but that you are there to help will go much further than cajoling or teasing the child about the fear.

The out of control child

All of the techniques discussed previously are geared to the prevention of uncooperative behavior. Practiced with consistency, these methods of interaction are proven effective. However, there is a small segment of the child population that is, in fact, out of control and very difficult to handle.

Children who exhibit out of control behavior often begin to throw a fit before they enter the treatment area or as soon as they enter the treatment area. The fit accelerates as the dentist enters the environment and increases as the doctor begins, or tries to begin, administering treatment. These children do not whimper. They howl. They do not squirm. They kick and fight. They do not protest. They try to escape.

This type of situation can prove to be trying, even exasperating, for even the most even-tempered doctor in the world. Don't think that you must win the battle at any cost. The "cost" could mean a lifetime of dental phobia for the child and psychological trauma that will be very difficult, if not impossible, to overcome. This type of no-win situation will often leave the dentist feeling guilty and unprofessional. If the child cannot be handled properly and comfortably, stop treatment and contact a specialist for advice and/or referral.

When to refer. In determining when a referral should be made, consider these three guidelines given by Dr. Litteken to his referring general practitioners:

- Know your limitations
- Know your level of tolerance
- Be able to assess a situation objectively. Stop or make changes, if necessary

When a general practitioner is referring a child to a pediatric specialist, a history of the child should be given. This history should include such information as:

- What has been comfortable for the child?
- What has not been comfortable?

Describe both the clinical and the behavioral history of the child. This information will help the pediatric dentist and his/her team to be better prepared for the child's arrival.

The protesting child

This is the child who is resistant to all that you ask of him/her. The child protests any procedures or any requests for cooperation.

Dr. Bozalis indicates that three difficult situations posed by the defiant or resistant child are:

- Making too much noise—screaming, hollering, crying
- Refusing to open his/her mouth
- Not sitting still during treatment

Efforts to coax or bribe the child or to use adult logic with the child are usually of no use.

In some situations, reverse psychology is effective. To use this technique, begin by actively listening to the child's behavior. Reflect back to the child what you perceive him/her to be feeling. For example: "You don't want to let me look at your teeth." or "You are feeling angry, and you want me to know that you are angry." You will usually grasp the child's attention with this type of reflective listening.

At this point, begin implementing the reverse psychology by encouraging the child to go ahead with the behavior.

For example: "Show me how mad you can become." "Throw a bigger fit." "Hit the chair." "Stick your tongue out at me." The child will usually go ahead with the prescribed behavior, but will quickly tire of this because the behavior is not getting the desired result. The dentist isn't getting angry at all but instead is encouraging the performance. Some children will find the situation humorous and will end it by laughing at the situation and at themselves. Continue this scenario until the child is ready to depart from the defiant behavior and enter a more cooperative state (Fig. 8-3).

COMMUNICATING
WITH CHILDREN PATIENTS

DOs

1. Compliment good behavior. Give positive reinforcement
2. Give specific instructions
3. Ask open-ended questions to discover the child's feelings
4. Plan a great initial visit
5. Ignore negative behavior
6. Give the child comforting physical contact—pats, strokes
7. Gradually proceed with treatment based on the child's readiness
8. Have short appointments or appointments that fit the child's tolerance level
9. Control yourself and your temper
10. Involve the child when possible. Let him/her be a helper
11. Carefully evaluate your facility, your appearance, and your systems
12. Send a pre-appointment letter
13. Refer when appropriate

DON'Ts

1. Treat children if you have no tolerance for them
2. Bribe a child
3. Force the child or make threats to the child
4. Ignore the child
5. Humiliate the child or put him/her down
6. Use physical force

Fig. 8-3: DO's and DON'Ts

COMMUNICATING WITH THE GERIATRIC PATIENT

Our *daily input* of media via television, telephone, computer, etc. is more than our grandparents received in a lifetime! Therefore you must not expect your geriatric patients to meet you where you are coming from, but rather you must meet them where they are. The following are some suggestions for assisting your geriatric patients:

- Upon entrance of a nursing home patient, the person administering your business office should *go to* the reception area to assure the comfort of the patient
- Provide access to your facility that does not make it difficult or impossible for a patient to achieve entrance
- If this person is a new patient, the necessary paperwork should be sent to the nursing home before the patient's visit, so that the attending staff can complete this paperwork while the records are in front of them
- If, for some reason, the necessary paperwork has not been completed, stop what you are doing, and go to the reception area to assist with the completion of the data
- Depending on the age and hearing ability of the patient, you may need to slow your speech somewhat, repeat what you have said to clarify, and speak a bit louder
- Assist the patient into and out of the dental chair. Gently tell the patient you will be lowering the chair *before* you lower it!
- Touching is so vital to people! Firmly and gently touch these wonderful individuals to let them know you care, to give them assurance and security, and to add a sense of warmth to their experience with you
- Treat these patients with extra attention in a mature, respectful, adult manner
- Always give the patient the opportunity to spend a few moments in the restroom (assisted, if necessary)
- Along with the nursing home attendant or family member (whoever brings the patient to the office), escort the patient to the front door or to the car. The value of this extra attention, courtesy, and assistance is immeasurable
- All patients need and deserve excellent and special attention, but these folks need a little extra. You could be a bright spot in their lonely days. You will give extra attention to them, but you will be the ultimate receiver

KEYPOINT:
....

Concentrate on
the prevention
of behavior problems
just as you concentrate
on the prevention
of disease.

IN SUMMARY

Children can be the most difficult of all your patients, and/or they can be one of your greatest sources of joy. Study this chapter, and look for concepts you can apply to your own practice. Begin to implement the ideas on a regular basis until they become a natural part of your patient management format.

The effects of a negative dental experience during childhood can be as ravaging as tooth decay! When you make a concerted effort to prevent fear in each young patient, you will be providing a lifetime gift to that person.

Develop a level of confidence with your children, with your geriatric patients, and with any special people who have special needs. Your confidence and the confidence of your team will have a powerful and reassuring effect on these valuable patients. Maintain self control at all times. Give your special patient your sincere love and attention. They will mirror that love and attention back to you.

COMMUNICATION
VIA THE TELEPHONE

*The telephone is the most important marketing tool
you have in your practice. Give it the respect it deserves
and the attention it needs.*

— DR. JOHN JAMESON

Your telephone is your artery to the world. Conversations held on the telephone make a statement about who you are, what you do, and how you take care of your clients/patients. That's why every time a member of the team is on the telephone, he/she is representing the practice. They ARE the practice to that caller. Make sure that each and every time you pick up a phone for an inbound or outbound call, you handle that call with care and attention.

In most cases, the telephone is the first contact with the practice. We all know about the importance of that first impression. Within about two minutes, a person has decided whether or not to like you or whether or not you know what you are doing. Any time a member of the team picks up the telephone for either an incoming or outgoing call, that team member must focus on the business at hand:

- Greeting the person on the phone
- Establishing the need of the caller
- Listening attentively
- Responding to the determined needs

Creating a positive impression on the telephone comes easily to some people and is easiest when you're in a good mood. However, the caller really doesn't care if you are in a good mood or not. They want to know that you are there to take care of them. Therefore, the key to excellent telephone etiquette is consistently making a positive impression. Before you answer the phone, take a deep breath (or two), smile, and get ready to greet the caller pleasantly and professionally.

TONE OF VOICE

In Chapter 5, I addressed the importance of tone of voice whether you are sending or receiving a message. Remember that when you are face to face with a person, tone of voice accounts for 30% of the perception of a message. On the telephone, tone of voice accounts for 90% of the perception of a message—whether you are sending or receiving the message. Obviously, there is no body language. The words you speak are significant, but they only account for 10% of the perception of the message. Return to Chapter 5, and review the information on tone of voice. Practice these skills, and work on continuous improvement.

I have previously recommended that you record yourself and analyze your tone of voice. I certainly recommend that you record yourself on the telephone. How would you react to your voice if you were the caller? Have members of your team or family members listen to your tape, and give you constructive feedback. Don't be offended if they make recommendations— be receptive to constructive coaching.

On the flip side of this, pay attention to the tone of voice of the caller. If you sense a strong emotion, become a good listener. Use active listening to make sure you are hearing the caller accurately and also to defuse or deflood their strong emotion, whatever that emotion might be.

ANSWERING THE TELEPHONE

The answering of the telephone should be a high priority. When the telephone rings, answer it between the second and third ring. Follow the suggestion of Bell Telephone and answer the telephone in the following manner: "Good Morning. Dr. Jameson's office. This is Cathy. How may I help you?"

By greeting the person in this manner you serve several purposes:

- This gives the person a pleasant, warm, enthusiastic greeting, offsetting perhaps, a negative attitude about calling the dentist
- You let the caller know that he/she has reached the correct number
- You give the person a name (your name) to attach to the voice (so he/she doesn't have to play a guessing game: Is this Mary? No. Is this Susie? No, etc.)
- You begin building a relationship from the initial contact
- You have asked the person if you can help, which, after all, is what you are there to do

If the telephone rings, and you are with a patient, courteously excuse yourself and answer the phone. If, in establishing the caller's need, you discover that you will need a few minutes to respond to them, ask if you may have a name and telephone number to call back. (If you do this, be sure to call back!)

For example: "Mrs. Jones, I am going to need a few minutes to discuss this insurance issue with you. I am with a patient at the moment. May I take your telephone number and return your call? Thank you. That's 555-6011. Okay, Mrs. Jones, I will return your call in (give a reasonable range) minutes. I appreciate your understanding."

If you have *almost* completed your tasks with the patient at the desk, you can *ask* the caller if you may place them on hold. Notice that I said to ask the caller if you may place them on hold. A person usually doesn't mind being placed on hold if asked rather than told.

For example: "Mr. Sanders, may I place you on hold for just a moment?" (Wait for his response.) "Thank you" If he says "no," take a name and telephone number and call him back immediately.

If you do place a person on hold, pick up the phone every 30 seconds or so, and let them know you haven't forgotten them.

For example: "Mr. Sanders, I'll be with you in just a few moments. Okay?"

When you do return to give your full attention to the caller, thank the person for his patience.

For example: "Mr. Sanders? Thank you for your patience. How may I help you?"

GETTING THE INFORMATION RIGHT

When you are taking messages or gathering patient information, make sure you gather the correct information. Each of these types of telephone communication is so vital that each deserves specific attention.

TAKING MESSAGES

When an incoming caller asks for the doctor or a member of the team, the general policy should be:

- the status of the person being called should be given (is he/she busy or not?)
- if he/she is busy, a name and phone number are taken on a message pad that has duplicate ability
- the appropriate message is taken
- the information is confirmed
- the message is placed in a designated location for convenient retrieval

For example: "I'm sorry, Mary is with a patient at this time. May I take your name and telephone number? I will ask Mary to return your call as quickly as possible. That's Jack Smith (get last name also) at Ace Office Supply, 555-4210. Is that correct? Thank you, Jack. I'll give Mary this message."

Be sure to repeat the message to clarify and ensure that you have taken the message correctly. Make sure Mary gets the message! Have a specific bin or a specific bulletin board where messages are placed. The business administrator doesn't have time to get up and deliver every message that comes through. These interruptions can have a negative impact on his or her productivity and focus. Plus, a messenger shouldn't be coming back to the clinical area and interrupting the clinical team. Every interruption takes energy—for unfocusing, responding, and refocusing. In addition, patients resent the interruption. They want the clinician's undivided attention. They don't want her/him to be distracted from their procedure.

That's why I recommend that you place a bulletin board or bin in a convenient location for the business administrator. He or she will take thorough messages and place the message where designated. Then it becomes the responsibility of team members to retrieve their messages and return their own calls (certainly, emergencies are the exception) (Fig. 9-1).

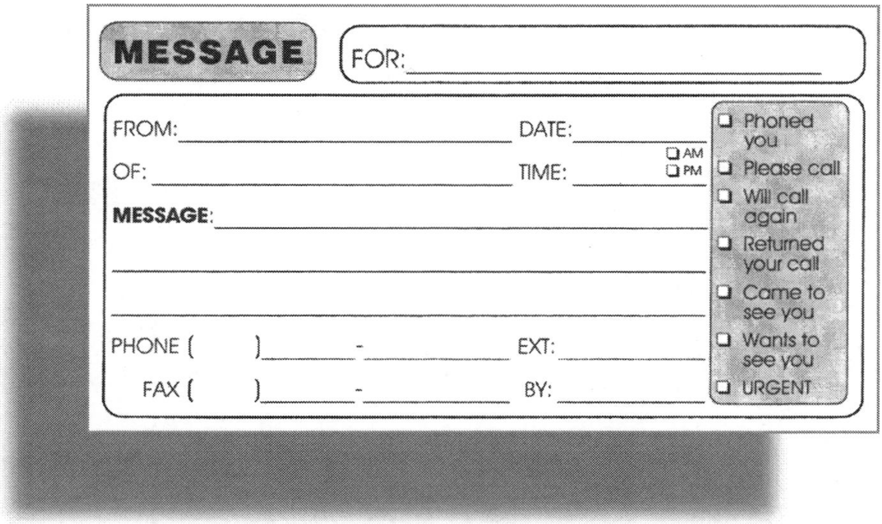

Fig. 9-1: Telephone Message Pad

This scenario serves the following purposes:

- You've graciously let the person know that the recipient of the call is unavailable, but that they can count on you to deliver the message
- Name and number of caller have been gathered, and you have repeated this information to ensure that the information is correct
- You have a specific location to post messages, so that the message is received. If this does not happen, both parties lose

- You've applied professional management to a vital area of the practice

PERSONAL TELEPHONE CALLS MUST BE LIMITED

These calls can be very costly to the practice in terms of time and money. Personal phone calls cause:

- lost production time—this applies to the business as well as the clinical team
- interference of the schedule that can negatively affect many people
- long distance bills to the office—in some practices, this applies

Some calls are passed on to the doctor for him/her to make a decision about whether or not the call is to be taken. However, the doctor should let the business administrator know which calls will be received in advance (i.e., specific referring doctors). Otherwise, apply careful screening and monitoring of all calls.

GATHERING PATIENT INFORMATION

Gathering and recording information from certain telephone calls are vital for "linkage communication"—communication that gets appropriate information from the business team to the clinical team. The Patient Communication Slip is an example of the type of information that should be gathered in two different instances—when a new patient calls your office and when an emergency calls (Fig. 9-2).

The new patient

When a person calls, and you do not recognize the name, ask the following: "When was the last time you saw Dr. Jameson?" rather than, "Are you a new patient?"

You try your best to remember people, but if you are new to the practice or if you have a slip of memory, you may forget a person's name. But a caller may be offended if he/she has been with the practice for a while, and you ask, "Are you a new patient?" Once a person has come into the practice, he/she expects you to remember them forever. People like to be remembered.

PATIENT COMMUNICATION SLIP

Date: _____ New Patient ❑ Patient of Record ❑ Adult ❑ Child ❑ Age _____

Name: _____ _____
                                                    (Pronounced)

Referred By: _____ Family Member ❑ Friend ❑ Parent/Guardian of Child: _____

Address: _____
            (Street)   (City)   (State)   (Zip)

Daytime Phone: _____ Home Phone: _____

Work Phone: _____ Email Address: _____

Purpose of Call

Emergency ❑ How long? _____	New Patient Evaluation ❑ Last time seen by a dentist? _____
Where is the problem located? _____	Date of FMS: _____ Doctor's Name: _____
Swelling? _____	Explain scenario of new patient evaluation: _____
Sensitive to hot/cold? _____	1. Hard & soft tissue evaluation: _____
Other: _____	2. Necessary Radiographs: _____
Premedication Necessary: _____	3. No cleaning: _____
Employer: _____	4. Statement of philosophy: _____
Insurance Carrier: _____	5. Question & Answer: _____
Policy Number: _____	6. Statement of payment expectations: _____
Comments: _____	7. New Patient Packet Sent: _____

©Jameson Management, Inc.

Fig. 9-2: Patient Communication Slip

Once you have determined that this is indeed a new patient, get out your pad of communication slips and begin recording relevant information. As soon as the person gives his/her name, write it down. If the name is somewhat unusual or difficult, write a phonetic spelling of the name and repeat it to make sure you are pronouncing it correctly. People like to have their names spelled and pronounced accurately. Then, throughout your conversation, ask appropriate questions and fill in the information. Repeat the person's name several times throughout the conversation. This gives a person a special sense of priority with you.

Before you start asking the questions or gathering the information, tell the person why you are gathering the information so he/she won't become irritated. This probably is your first contact with this person. The last thing in the world you want to be is irritating. Sell the person on the benefits of your information gathering process.

For example: "Mrs. Jones, we are so glad that you have called. Dr. Jameson is great. You will be so glad that you have chosen to come here. Mrs. Jones, we want to be fully and carefully prepared for your appointment, so may I ask you some questions so we can have everything ready for you?"

The communication slip acts much like a script. You will be guided through the phone call, and you will not forget to ask important questions.

Having this information at the outset gives you a head start in preparing the necessary paperwork for the person's arrival at your office. It also gives you a common base upon which to build rapport with this new patient on their initial visit. You will be able to give your clinical team information about the new patient in advance. All of you will be able to roll out the red carpet.

Emergencies

When a person calls and indicates that they have an emergency situation, again get out your patient communication slip and begin taking down relevant information. Find out what kinds of things your doctor wants to know about the emergency patient to determine if this is truly an emergency and something about the situation so that the clinical team can be prepared. Use a professionally produced form, such as Figure 9.2, or create your own.

When you have gathered this information, either provide the necessary information at your morning meeting, or if the emergency patient calls after the morning meeting, get the communication slip to the clinical team as quickly as possible. Do not ask your clinical team to see an emergency patient not knowing anything about the situation prior to his/her arrival. Both the clinicians and the patient will be better served by having the information in advance.

TELEPHONE COMMUNICATION:
THE BOTTOM LINE TO INCREASED REVENUES

Enhanced telephone communication can increase the revenues of your practice. Let's look further into the value of telephone communication as a practice builder and as a way to increase production.

Cathy, I want you to come to my study club to deliver a seminar on telephone communication. There is so much that can and should be done on the telephone to make the practice stronger. It seems to me that there is a big difference between someone getting on the phone and calling down a list of people to schedule hygiene appointments and someone making excellent telephone calls that really let people/patients know that you care and that you are concerned.

The goal, it would seem, is the scheduling of the appointment. However, that is a great deal more difficult than it seems. There are specific skills that can and should be learned to turn tele-marketing into tele-relations in the dental office. Come and teach us those skills.

That was the thrust of an energetic conversation I had with Dr. Mitch Cantor. Dr. Cantor wisely understands that when a member of the team is on the telephone, he/she can make or break a relationship with a patient and can certainly have a strong impact on whether or not a person schedules an appointment. Marketing data have shown that 7 out of 10 patients make a decision as to whether or not they will schedule an appointment by how they are handled on the telephone. A marketing tool? Yes! An important one.

In this portion of the chapter on telephone communication, the critical factors of scheduling an appointment over the phone will be detailed. I will also give you some armamentarium that may prove helpful in stimulating interest in the appointment even if the patient is originally less than enthusiastic.

SCHEDULING AN APPOINTMENT OVER THE TELEPHONE

When you are on the telephone trying to schedule an appointment for the hygienist or for the doctor, you are in essence making a sales call. You are selling the benefits of the appointment. The goal of this sales call is to schedule the appointment.

Without question, you believe that the scheduling of the appointment is important or you wouldn't be making the call in the first place. A strong belief in the benefits of your services gives the appointment effort greater strength—strength that is driven by your sincere concern for the patient.

FOUR STAGES OF AN EFFECTIVE TELEPHONE CALL

There are four stages of any call cycle. Each type of telephone call has the same four stages:

- Opening
- Gathering information
- Presentation
- Closing

Learning how to effectively move through these four stages to reach your goal of scheduling the appointment will give you a much higher success rate.

Stage 1: The opening

You may encounter an objection right from the beginning. Therefore, your opening is critical. If you do receive objections right from the start, you have to be poised to open the door and keep it open.

Why would you get objections at the opening of your call? You may be "an interruption." That is one of the things that must be realized about the telephone. Some people view a telephone call as an interruption. Therefore, you must deal effectively with this.

I encourage you to use scripts for reference. Carefully planned and practiced scripts (appropriate for the different types of calls you will be making) will give you the verbal skills and the confidence necessary to carry out an excellent telephone call.

Don't shoot from the hip. This will get you backed into a corner more times than not. Be well prepared. The scripts will prove to be a wonderful and useful road map. You must personalize the scripts to fit you and your situation. The scripts must include an opening that will stimulate interest on the part of the patient. They must also include convincing responses not only to objections, but also for such intermediate queries as "tell me more." In other words, be prepared.

In the opening sequence of your telephone call, you only have a few seconds to qualify a person as someone who is interested in scheduling an appointment or to turn an objection around.

Here is an example of an opening statement for a hygiene retention telephone call:

Hygiene Coordinator: "Mrs. Jones, this is Cathy with Dr. Jameson's dental office. I'm so glad I reached you today. Mrs. Jones, Dr. Jameson has been reviewing your records, and finds that it has been seven months since your last dental cleaning and evaluation, and he was concerned. The last time you were here, which was in October of last year, the doctor indicated a concern about the puffiness in some of your gum tissue. He asked that I call you today to schedule an appointment not only for your professional dental cleaning but also for him to evaluate those areas of concern. Tell me which is better for you, mornings or afternoons?"

The hygiene coordinator has led into the conversation in a very affirmative, positive manner. If the patient is interested in scheduling an appointment, the coordinator has done all the right things to open that door. Notice that she did not set herself up for a "no" by saying something like, "Do you want to schedule an appointment?" She controlled the entire conversation, but let the patient feel that she was in control. She was very prepared for the phone call. She knew how long it had been since the patient's last visit. She knew something the doctor had expressed a concern about and mentioned that to the patient. She let the patient know this was an individualized call and that she knew something personal about the patient's situation. Plus, she stressed the value and importance of the appointment.

However, if the patient doesn't seem overly interested in scheduling and begins to pose objections, the coordinator must be prepared to move the direction of the conversation into a more positive arena. She can do this by introducing the "basic turnaround."

Basic turnaround. The basic turnaround is a way to communicate to your patients that you have heard their objection to the scheduling of the appointment and that you understand their concern. The basic turnaround allows you to continue moving in a forward direction by introducing something new to the patient. In other words, you begin to turn that objection from a negative into a positive result.

Steps of the basic turnaround:

Step one—Tell the person that you have previously heard their objection from people who ended up going ahead with your services

Step two—Introduce a new proposal

After your opening statement or your initial effort to schedule an appointment, the patient may object. When they say they're not interested, restructure your opening, and ask their permission to go on. Then, introduce something new.

Gain permission to ask a couple of questions in order to evaluate the patient's position. This is critical. You must qualify the person. In other words, you must know something about their concerns or their wants. Once you have this insight, you can decide which new proposal you will offer.

For example:

> **Patient:** "Oh, I know I need to come in, but I just don't have time right now and money is pretty tight for me here at tax time"

> **Hygiene Coordinator:** "Your schedule is quite hectic, I know, and I understand the tax problem. (Active listening.) Mrs. Jones, may I ask you one quick question?" (This helps the person focus on the proposal rather than on their objection.)

Once you have received their permission to ask that question, do so. Ask a question that will open a new door. Introduce something new to the patient, something beyond the original reason for the telephone call.

It could prove effective to use the "feel, felt, found" here.

> **Hygiene Coordinator:** "Mrs. Jones, I understand how you *feel* about investing in dental care at this time of the year. Many of our patients have *felt* the same way and have expressed a concern this year. Then they *found* that, in our practice, we have a convenient method of extended payment allowing you to receive the care that you need without putting financial stress on you. You can finance your needed dental care and spread the payments out over a period of time keeping those payments small and reasonable. With this new method of payment, you can stay on a regular program of hygiene and health but not stress yourself out financially. Would this be of interest to you?"

This does the following:

- It lets the patient know that you empathize with them and that you are not upset with them for their feelings or concerns
- You let them know that they are not the only person in your practice who has experienced these concerns

- You let the person know that other people have found a solution to the objection

Prepare carefully for any sequence of telephone contacts—different telephone calls for different types of scheduling scenarios. Identify normal objections that come up on a regular basis. Write scripts that you can use to effectively deal with these objections. Integrate the basic turn-around into these scripts. This will give you flexibility and the ability to forecast problems ahead of time. It is better to be prepared than to be blindsided by an objection.

Stage 2: Gathering information

Seventy-five percent of the actual process of scheduling a presentation takes place at this point.

This is where the professional is distinguished from the amateur. You must:

- gather information from the patient's perspective
- know how much detail is appropriate
- uncover the objections
- figure out the patient's level of knowledge about your services

This is where you earn the right to make a presentation!

Let the patient perceive that you care. You are there to solve problems and to change smiles.

For example:

Treatment Coordinator: (making follow-up telephone calls to people who have dentistry diagnosed but left untreated): "Mrs. Jones, this is Jan with Dr. Jameson's dental office. I'm

KEYPOINT:

The key to success is to ask questions and listen!

glad I am able to reach you. Mrs. Jones, last week during our consultation appointment, you told me that you needed to speak with your husband about the treatment Dr. Jameson had recommended to you. We were sorry that he was ill and could not come with you to the consultation. What did he think of the photographs from our imaging system that we sent home with you?"

Listen to response.

"Mrs. Jones, as you had requested, I am calling this week to see if you or your husband have any questions about the treatment that Dr. Jameson has recommended. I know this is the type of treatment you would like to receive, and we want to do everything we can to make that possible for you. What questions do you have?"

If, for any reason, a person doesn't schedule an appointment at the end of a consultation, at a hygiene appointment, or whenever there is dentistry diagnosed but left untreated, ask the patient for permission to call them back. If a patient says, "Oh, I'll call you," know that the patient has just spoken the three most non-productive words in dentistry—"I'll call you."—because they won't!

If a patient says they will call you, respond in the following manner:

Treatment Coordinator: "Thank you, Mrs. Jones, for offering. However, since it is our responsibility to take good care of you, if it's all right with you, I'll call in the next week or two to see if you have any questions. Would that be okay?" (They will more than likely say yes.) "Tell me, Mrs. Jones, should I call you next week or do you prefer that I call you the week after?" Offer her an alternative of choice—two options, either answer of which you are going to like. Make a note to yourself in your tickler system, whether manual or in the computer, to make that call and be sure you do so.

Notice in the above scenario the treatment coordinator opened her conversation courteously, reminding the patient that she had requested the call. Then she very encouragingly and positively opened the door for questions. Remember: she is looking for objections. Once these objections are on the table, she has a chance to overcome each and every one of them.

Unless she identifies those objections by asking questions, she doesn't have a chance to overcome them.

Stage 3: Presentation

During this phase of the telephone contact, once you have earned the right to make the presentation, you must gain the person's trust and confidence, and you must stimulate interest. Remember: a person will buy what they want long before buying what they need. Therefore, in order to access the attention you will need to schedule the appointment, you will have to key in to the person's wants, or their "motivational hot buttons."

As you present the possibility of scheduling an appointment, you must stress the benefits of that appointment. You cannot do this unless you have asked careful questions and have determined what that particular patient's needs might be. You must then be prepared to give proof that your practice and your doctor or hygienist can meet those needs. One of the most effective ways to do this is to use examples or testimonial stories of other patients.

For example:

Mrs. Jones: "Yes, we looked at those pictures, and my husband sees the mess in my mouth, but he isn't sure that my mouth can be fixed! And he sure doesn't want to spend the money to do so!"

Treatment Coordinator: "Mr. Jones isn't clear about the treatment that Dr. Jameson is recommending to restore your mouth, and he wonders if we can get results that you will be happy with, is that right?"

Mrs. Jones:: "Yes, that's right. He thinks I'm hopeless"

Treatment Coordinator: "Have you had a chance to show Mr. Jones the before and after photographs of the case that is similar to yours? I think he will be pleased to see that other people who have been in a critical situation such as yours have had their mouths restored. They look great, chew well, feel fabulous, and are much healthier and a lot happier"

Mrs. Jones: "Yes, I showed him. He was pretty amazed, but he still thinks it's too much money."

KEYPOINT:

If you do not call for a decision, you are giving your patients permission to procrastinate.

Treatment Coordinator: "Please show him the information I gave you about our financial programs. Then, if it's okay, I'll call in a few days to answer any questions about your treatment or about our financial options. Should I call Tuesday, or would Wednesday be better?"

Then, she would make a note to herself to call again when the patient requested.

Stage 4: Closing

Your goal is to schedule an appointment. This is the "closing." Actually, closing starts at the beginning. It is a natural part of the sequence. When all concerns and objections have been identified and overcome, then close.

Closing means that you ask the patient for a commitment to proceed. You need to ask a patient to proceed. They are often looking for help in making that decision. Most people cannot or choose not to make decisions.

Ask them to proceed. Ask them to schedule that appointment. If you sincerely believe in the dental care you are providing, who loses if the patient falls out of treatment?

For example:

Treatment Coordinator: (after she has made the next telephone call, answered all questions of Mr. and Mrs. Jones, and has discussed the available financial options): "Mrs. Jones, do you have any further questions about the treatment or about the financial responsibility? No? Then, let's go ahead and schedule your first appointment. Do you prefer mornings or afternoons?"

Helpful Hints For Effective Appointment Scheduling

1. Be sincere
2. Slow your speech
3. Use scripts
4. Listen, listen, listen
5. Mentally review positives and negatives, and be prepared to address them
6. Speak in layman's language
7. Monitor and record the results of your calls

Tracking your phone calls will allow you to analyze your progress (Fig. 9-3).

This will also let you know if you are on target and getting great results or if you need to make adjustments. If your tracking indicates that great

Jameson management inc.						J
Retention Telephone Calls						
Date	Time	Dials	Completed Calls	Appts. Made	Negative Responses	Comments
					© Jameson management, Inc.

Fig. 9-3: Telephone Tracking Device

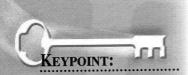

KEYPOINT:

Track your telephone calls and contacts.

results are not being gained, then make necessary changes. Don't keep doing something if it isn't working for you. Even though you may get answering machines, disconnects and/or people who won't schedule, these are all stepping stones to success. Keep trying. The odds will be in your favor (Fig. 9-4).

MINDSET

One of the keys to great success in telephone scheduling is to keep trying. Keep calling. The bigger your net, the more fish you will catch. Some people are going to slip away, but when you accept these as a part of the overall process, you can see your efforts in proper perspective.

Don't get discouraged. Don't quit, even though you may get several rejections in a row. Keep imagining that the next person will say "yes." One of the greatest assets to success in scheduling appointments over the telephone is your own initiative and motivation.

HELPFUL HINTS

1. **Track your numbers.** Don't do any telephone work without monitoring your results.
2. **Set specific goals.** For example: try to reach decision-makers 50% of the time. Try to schedule at least 50% of your calls.
3. **Note productive times for calling.** Make sure that you are calling during the "high" times of the day. The only way you will know those best times is to track it.
4. **Get all possible numbers of where and how a person can be reached**. Ask the patient how you can best reach them: home, work, fax, cell phone, e-mail. Whatever it takes.

Fig. 9-4: Helpful Hints for Telephone Use

Constantly give yourself positive affirmations such as:

- our services are needed by our patients
- I am confident
- this will be a great day
- this is the practice
- I can do whatever I decide to do

WHEN MAKING TELEPHONE CALLS

- get ready
- warm up
- get mentally prepared
- know your product and service
- describe these in patient terms
- use simple, everyday language
- know your practice

Three qualities to project in your telephone calls are:

- competency
- authority
- control

Don't take rejections personally. Use the graphs. See your progress. See the results of your efforts. Know that if a person does not schedule an appointment and you have done the best you can possibly do, it is the proposal that is being rejected, not you. It is only through commitment to the ongoing process of personal development that you will get the results you want.

KEYPOINT:

The law of averages will be in your favor if you keep trying.

KEYPOINT:

Motivation is defined in the following manner:

"Affecting the environment in such a way that your efforts will be more productive."

HOW DO YOU HANDLE
THE IRATE CALLER?

I'm sure that by now you agree with me that telephone skills are critical to establishing and maintaining excellent relationships with patients. But sometimes that's not easy! From time to time, an angry or irate patient calls and tests your telephone skills, your people skills, and your patience! How do you effectively deal with an irate person when they call you on the phone?

Here's what to do!

Hear the person out. Don't interrupt with questions, comebacks, or defensive responses. Passively listen. That means, encourage them to "go on," to "spill their guts," to "get it all out!"

You passively listen by saying things such as:

- "I see"
- "tell me more"
- "please, explain what you mean"
- "oh, really?"
- "I understand"
- "I agree"
- "I know"
- "you have every right to feel that way"

Try to agree with the caller when possible.

Actively listen. The single most effective skill you can use to defuse anger and calm the irate person is to listen to them. Encourage a person to tell you about their concern. Reflect to the person (in your own words) what you think you hear them saying. This will give you a chance to clarify and let the person know that you are trying to understand. This will also calm him/her down.

Do not argue with the person. This will only add fuel to the fire. Your defensiveness will add to their defensiveness. The emotionality of the conversation will become so intense that the possibility of moving into a problem-solving mode may be nullified.

Control your urge to become angry! A person can't stay angry with you if you remain calm. Your calmness will help them sense your respect and your concern about the problem and that you want to hear all about it so you can do something. If a person senses your willingness to listen and to work on the resolution of the problem, he/she will be more inclined to work with you in return.

Once you've heard a person out, you've passively and actively listened, and you've defused their anger by not being negatively stimulated, say thank you to the person for letting you know about the problem (and mean it!) "Thank you for calling, Mr. Johnson. I am so glad to know that you have a concern. I really want to help you. I appreciate your honesty."

Ask Mr. Johnson to repeat his concerns so that you can write them down. "Mr. Johnson, would you please repeat your concerns for me? I am going to write these down so I can determine if I can help you and to make sure I accurately inform Dr. Jameson of your concerns"

Once you have recorded the necessary information, repeat it to him to determine that your interpretation was correct. Let him know that you understand his concerns and that you will do your best to find appropriate answers. Tell him that you will get back to him and then do so! "Mr. Johnson, I understand your confusion over this situation. Now that I have all of the correct information, I am going to discuss this with Dr. Jameson, and we will do our best to find an answer to your questions. I will get back to you within the next couple of days. Would you prefer I call you at work, or would it be better if I call you at home?"

Do what you say you will do. Find the answers. Develop a solution. Make a note in your tickler system to get back to him at the time agreed upon. Then, do it!

GREAT RESULTS

If you will commit to going through these steps, you will find that most irate callers will calm down. Often, by the second time they have repeated their concerns, they will have either softened or answered their own questions. You will have deflooded some of their emotion by listening effectively.

A person will reflect your temperament. If you become angry, he/she will become angrier. If you slow your speech, lower your voice, and remain calm, he/she will reflect this. Only when the irate caller is calmed can a solution be generated.

A side benefit to this process is that you will not be so stressed out. If you become angry, your blood pressure will rise, your pulse will increase, and stress will negatively affect your day and your performance. However, if you choose to be the one in control, you will encourage a calmer patient, and you will control your own stress.

IN SUMMARY

It has been said that the telephone may be the most important instrument in your office. As such, the value of excellent telephone technique cannot be over-emphasized. The bottom line is this—you have a brief opportunity to educate and motivate a person to come to your practice.

Be informed about the policies and procedures of your office. A person makes an initial decision about the organization and services available in your office by their interaction with the person who answers the telephone. Therefore, everyone who speaks to clients/patients on the telephone for any reason must be adept at telephone skills.

We talk a great deal about marketing tools in dentistry. One the most valuable marketing tools in your office is the telephone. Use it carefully and powerfully.

MAKING AN EFFECTIVE
CASE PRESENTATION:
GAINING TREATMENT ACCEPTANCE

*People don't care how much you know
until they know how much you care about them.*

— ZIG ZIGLAR

*I*n the majority of today's dental practices, fabulous opportunities lie within the walls of these practices. Most dental practices can double the amount of dentistry presently being provided by nurturing that which they already have—their existing patient family. Excellent communication is the bottom line to great case presentations leading to treatment acceptance.

For some dental professionals, this is where the "rubber meets the road." They know that case presentation makes the ultimate difference, but they are extremely inadequate or uncomfortable with the communicative skills required to make a great case presentation. In addition, some teams who admit to not being where they want to be with their practices aren't aware of the fact that their presentation scenario is weak. They continue to "tell" people what they need, explaining everything very technically, and

KEYPOINT:

Most practices can double from within!

KEYPOINT:

Getting the dentistry out of the charts and into the mouths of your patients is critical for practice growth.

then wake up in the middle of the night thinking, "I wonder if Mr. Jones ever scheduled an appointment." Stressful!

The most crucial marketing strategy that a practice embraces—the one by which practice growth and stability begin and end—is to have a well-managed practice. Perhaps the most critical of these management strategies is the system of case acceptance. Here is the fulcrum of your practice—careful diagnosis, complete treatment planning, fabulous case presentations, and follow-up. Knowing how to do the dentistry is essential. However, knowing how to do it and getting to do it are sometimes two separate things!

Upon careful analysis, most practices have more dentistry sitting in the charts waiting to be done than they have ever provided!

In addition, it costs less to nurture an existing client than it does to access a new one.

Combine those two pieces of information. Develop a business plan that accomplishes the following:

- Doubles the practice by nurturing your own patient family
- Does this in a cost-effective manner

Treatment acceptance: The goals

Developing an effective protocol for your treatment presentations accomplishes the following goals:

- The patient outlines the goals he/she wants to accomplish
- Patients are educated about the need for and the benefits of the dental treatments that you are recommending
- Patients become motivated to accept those particular recommendations

The purpose of a case presentation protocol is to encourage patients to say "yes" to the treatment you are recommending. I believe so much in the dentistry that my husband, John, is providing that I hurt when a patient walks out the door not scheduling an appointment to proceed. I think that it is our responsibility to present the recommendations so excellently that the person will have every chance in the world to proceed. If we don't do a good job of presenting the case and the person does not schedule, I think the patient loses. Therefore, learning the sophisticated skills of case presentation is critical for both the success of the practice and the benefit of patients.

KEYPOINT:

The case acceptance protocol is not just one person's responsibility.

The team approach
to case acceptance

The case acceptance protocol is not just one person's responsibility. Everyone on the dental team has specific responsibilities.

It is not the responsibility of the doctor only. Everyone is critical. Everyone has dynamic responsibilities. Remember the moment of truth! Each person on the team can make or break a person's willingness to proceed with treatment.

I have studied with some of the great business consultants in America. Why? To gain insight into the strategies that lead to corporate success. I have listened to them with my "dental ears" and have tried to translate the information to our own industry. The steps of case presentation follow the format promoted by the great companies of the world. They know that if they want their products or services to be purchased by their consumers/clients, they have to study and improve presentation skills. So do we, as dental professionals. Here, indeed is the moment of truth: the case presentation. Study. Practice.

Make a commitment to learn these intricate skills so they are as comfortable for you as that crown prep!

This chapter on case presentation pulls together all the communication skills studied in previous chapters. Here you will see that the foundational communication skills become strong vehicles throughout the presentations. You must have a strong foundation before climbing to a higher level of expertise.

THE STEPS

Step 1: Build the Relationship

The first step of a case presentation is to build the relationship. Before a person will say "yes" to your recommendations, you must build a relationship of confidence and trust. Without this level of confidence and trust, you will not get to the point at which you can provide necessary treatment. Remember that the oral cavity is an intimate zone of the human body and deserves the ultimate respect. This is why establishment of trust is so critical.

Most of the time, the initial contact is made on the telephone. The telephone is a powerful marketing tool in your practice (see Chapter 9). People calling your dental office make a subconscious decision about the dental treatment they will receive by the treatment received on the telephone. In fact, they often make a decision about whether they will come to you or go to someone else based on their first impression. It is very important that the person answering the telephone be enthusiastic, warm, and knowledgeable. They must *concentrate* when answering the telephone and focus on the business at hand, which is the person on the other end of the line. Their goals are:

- to let a person know he/she has made a good decision by calling your practice
- to help them feel good about coming to you
- to solidify the appointment

The new patient

Upon answering the telephone, if you determine this is a new patient calling, immediately grab a new patient telephone communication slip and begin recording information about this newcomer (Fig. 9-2). You begin gathering information so you can be totally prepared for the patient's arrival and will know something about him/her before they arrive (Fig. 10-1).

Welcome packet

Send a packet of information to the new patient before their scheduled appointment. Why? To prepare for their arrival and acquaint them with you and your practice. Begin the bonding process in advance. (This will offset some of those new patient broken appointments and no shows!) In this "welcome packet," include the following:

Fig. 10-1: Initial Contact: The Telephone

- Patient information sheet/health history
- Confirmation card for the appointment (Fig. 10-2)
- Practice brochure or welcome letter (Fig. 10-3)
- Patient education newsletter or brochure about a service you provide, like a cosmetic brochure (Fig. 10-4)
- Self-addressed, stamped envelope
- Information/brochure about your patient financing program
- Smile evaluation form (Fig. 10-5)

Tell the patient that you will be sending some information about the office. Ask that the patient information sheet/health history be completed and mailed back to you in the enclosed envelope. Explain that by returning this information prior to the appointment, you can be better prepared for their visit and will be able to seat them more quickly. Sell the benefits of this request to the patient, and they will respond positively by sending the information back to you.

For example: "Mrs. Jones, I am going to be sending you some information about our practice. We want you to know about us before your visit. Included in your packet will be a brochure about our office, one of our

Fig. 10-2: (Below)
Welcome Card

Fig. 10-3: (Right)
Office Brochure

WELCOME
TO OUR OFFICE!

We're looking forward to meeting you!
Because you are a special person, we
will strive to make your visit with
us a unique and pleasant experience.

This time has been reserved especially for you...

Date:

JOHN H. JAMESON, DDS
101 Jameson Drive · Wynnewood, OK 73098
Phone: (405) 665-2041
©Jameson Management Group

JOHN H. JAMESON, DDS, INC.

newsletters, a card confirming your appointment, and your information sheet/health history. We ask that you complete this information sheet and return it to us in the self-addressed, stamped envelope that I am including. Most of our patients are much more comfortable completing this information sheet at home where they have all of the necessary data. Plus, when

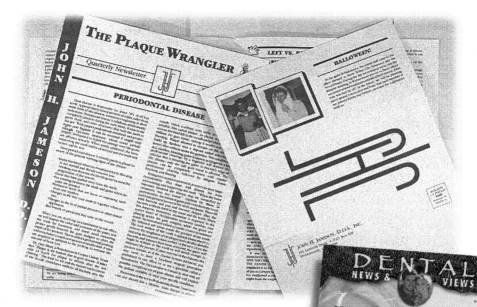

Fig. 10-4: Patient Education Newsletters

you return the information, Dr. Jameson will be able to review it before your appointment. By doing this, we can have all of your information in our computer and will be able to seat you more quickly."

In this conversation with the new patient, present your request in terms of how her compliance will benefit her—convenience, preparedness, and quicker seating. All of these issues are benefits to the patient. Know that you will get much further with any request if you present it in terms of how it benefits the other person. Remember: people want to know, "What's in this for me? How will this benefit me?"

Practice brochure

By enclosing a brochure about your office outlining the positive aspects of your practice, you can offset last minute cold feet (Fig. 10-3). In addition, you can build a person's confidence in you before they step foot inside your door. Don't just list the services you provide. Think of the brochure as a marketing tool for and about your practice.

A practice brochure needs the following components:

- Practice logo

- Color scheme that is consistent with all other written communication pieces
- Mission statement
- Sell the benefits of the services you offer. Don't make it a nagging piece about the things they have to do when they come to your office
- Open your own doors for the types of services you wish to develop in your practice
- Photograph and biography of the doctor/doctors to build confidence in them
- Address, as well as directions to the office (map, if appropriate)

PATIENT EDUCATION NEWSLETTERS

Surveys indicate that patients do like a personally produced newsletter. The newsletter should be brief and personal. Patients should sense that they are in direct contact with you, that you are sharing something special with them, and that you care about them as individuals.

You can accomplish the following goals with a patient newsletter:

- Be in the homes of each of your patient families in a positive way on a regular basis
- Inform and educate patients about what's happening in dentistry
- Let people know what you are doing in your own practice to stay on top of the latest and greatest in dentistry
- Express your appreciation for their confidence
- Ask for referrals

All members of the team can participate. One person can be in charge of the newsletter, but can delegate. At a team meeting, discuss the topics for the upcoming newsletter. Give assignments to the various members of the team who are to provide the copy. The doctor could write a brief article for the cover page. Other team members can volunteer to either write or bring an article from a magazine or news piece. If an article is

- Telephone numbers
- Office hours
- Attractive, to the point, encouraging, motivational, classy

Patient education newsletter

A patient education newsletter sets you apart from the average (Fig. 10-4). It lets people know something about the services you have available, and it lets people know of your total commitment to long-term

under 200 words, reprint is acceptable. If an article is more than 200 words, permission must be accessed, and credit must be given. By a certain date, everyone has the data to the person in charge. This person types or cuts and pastes the newsletter together.

In our own practice, we produce a one-page, legal size newsletter—front and back. It is short, sweet, informative, comfortable, and attractive. We do the entire piece with appropriate software on our computer. The softwares for personal publication are fabulous. Once you have created your piece, take the original copy to a print shop, and they will quickly and inexpensively produce the copies, fold them, and have them ready for you to label.

As you are producing your newsletter, be sure to place your return address, the bulk mailing number, and "address correction requested" on the outside fold.

Print your labels from the computer. At one staff meeting per quarter, the entire team can gather together over lunch, (doctor buys!) and attach the labels to the newsletters. Or hire a high school student to come to your office to do the labeling for you. If you are using a bulk mailing number, you must place the newsletters in zip code order. Again, your computer will do this for you.

The money you invest in a patient newsletter would be a part of your marketing and promotion budget. The time and money is well worth the effort. From each newsletter, you can generate new patients and a great deal of dentistry. Never lose sight of your number one goal—to educate your patients about the benefits of the dental services you provide. Remember: no one is going to educate your patients for you. The responsibility is yours.

care. You can produce one yourself or have a professionally produced newsletter. The professionally produced newsletters do make it possible for you to include individual information or a personalized article by your doctor or a member of your team.

Smile Evaluation

Jameson management inc.

1. Do you like the way your teeth look?   Yes ☐   No ☐
   Explain:_____

2. Are you happy with the color of your teeth?   Yes ☐   No ☐
   Explain:_____

3. Would you like for your teeth to be whiter?   Yes ☐   No ☐
   Explain:_____

4. Would you like your teeth to be straighter?   Yes ☐   No ☐
   Explain:_____

5. Do you have spaces between your teeth that you would like closed?   Yes ☐   No ☐
   If so, where?_____

6. Would you like your teeth to be longer?   Yes ☐   No ☐
   If so, Upper____ Lower_____ Both_____?

7. Do you like the shape of your teeth?   Yes ☐   No ☐
   Explain:_____

8. Do you have missing teeth that you would like to replace?   Yes ☐   No ☐
   Explain:_____

9. Do you have old silver fillings that you would like to replace with tooth-colored fillings?
   Yes ☐   No ☐
   Explain:_____

10. If you could change anything about your smile, what would you change?_____
    _____

© Jameson Management, Inc.

Fig. 10-5: Jameson Smile Evaluation Form

Marketing experts recommend that you stay in touch with your client/patient base every three months. Introduce something new to them every 90 days. That's easy in dentistry since patients really don't know much about any of the services offered. Plus, in dentistry, new and exciting opportunities happen on a regular basis.

Therefore, discuss something different every quarter—a specific dental technique, one of your management strategies, or a beneficial healthcare note. Address the total health of your patients not just the dental health.

Face to face contact

Building the relationship continues as the patient enters your practice for the first time. The person greeting the patient should stop what she is doing,

Fig. 10-6: Greeting the New Patient (Business Administrator)

stand up, and make a conscious effort to greet the patient by name. An introduction is desirable. Apply the same etiquette you use in your home to the dental practice.

For example: "Mrs. Jones? I'm Cathy. I spoke with you on the telephone. Welcome to our practice. We're glad you are here. Thank you for returning your information to us. Since we have all of the necessary information, the doctor is ready for you. Make yourself comfortable for just a moment, and I will let the team know you are here. By the way, I notice that John Smith referred you to our practice. He's great. We really appreciate him telling you about us." (Fig. 10-6).

Usually the next person that a patient meets is the clinical assistant. I encourage the clinical assistant to address the person in this way: "Mrs. Jones, I'm Donna, Dr. Jameson's clinical assistant. Welcome to our practice. I'm so glad to meet you. I will be working with you and with Dr. Jameson today. You may come with me now." (Fig. 10-7).

Fig. 10-7: Greeting the New Patient (The Clinical Assistant)

Then the clinical assistant escorts the person to the consultation room or to the clinical area. Here she reviews the health history, making sure it is complete, asks some pertinent questions, and lets the person know that she wants to get to know them as an individual and that she needs to be aware of anything that might affect upcoming treatment.

Tell the patient a bit about the philosophy of the practice, and describe what will be happening today. It is very important for a person to know what is going to happen before it happens. The clinical assistant can briefly go through the scenario of the initial evaluation, making sure the person is informed and comfortable.

Upon the entrance of the doctor, the clinical assistant makes an introduction. If, for some reason, the clinical assistant is not in the room, then the doctor should introduce him/herself.

Clinical Assistant: "Mrs. Jones, this is Doctor Jameson. Doctor Jameson, I'd like to introduce you to Mary Jones."

The initial interview begins. The clinical assistant could provide a bit of appropriate information about Mrs. Jones so the doctor can comfortably begin the conversation. The referral source is a good starting point. During this initial interview, be keenly aware of body language. Sit on the same level. Try not to have anything between you and the patient. Establish and maintain eye contact.

STEP 2: ESTABLISH THE NEED

Step 2 of an effective presentation is to establish the need. This involves not only determining the clinical needs in the patient's mouth, but also his/her emotional needs. As I have said previously, most people make a buying decision emotionally and then back that decision up with logic. In order for you to help a person make a decision to go ahead with treatment, you must determine his/her "perceived" or "felt" need. People will buy what they want long before they will buy what they need. Your responsibility in your initial interview is to determine that "felt need." You do this by asking questions and listening.

Your patient information sheet should have questions patients can answer about their attitude toward their dental health or the appearance of their smile. Patient questionnaires or smile evaluations can give you valuable information about a person's interests. In addition, your information sheet, questionnaires, or evaluations can open the doors to treatment possibilities (e.g., cosmetic possibilities) by stimulating thought processes. The questionnaire is geared toward the patient's dental needs.

INITIAL INTERVIEW

During your initial interview, ask open-ended questions that give the person a chance to tell you what he/she wants and to begin feeling confident in your relationship. By asking questions and listening, you gain valuable information and insight. You gain control of a conversation by asking questions, but at the same time, you give the patient that needed *sense of control.*

PATIENT QUESTIONNAIRES

Develop a questionnaire for your new and existing patients. As a part of each new patient's first appointment, ask him or her to complete this questionnaire. Or, send it along with your welcome packet, asking them to complete the questions, then return it in the self-addressed, stamped envelope provided or bring it in to the office when they come in for their initial visit.

For your existing patients, tell them that you are continually trying to improve your services and want to add treatment options to meet their needs. Therefore, in order to do that, you would like them to take a couple of minutes to complete a brief questionnaire. Present the questionnaire to your patients on your letterhead stationery on a clipboard with a good pen.

Make sure that you respond to a patient's answers. This is a wonderful chance to let a person feel comfortable sharing their thoughts and feelings about their smile. This could open doors for you to provide many services, including, but not limited to, cosmetic treatment. Patients will be happy to fill this out if you let them know that you are doing this to better serve them.

Again, if you do ask written questions of your patients, be sure to respond to their answers. This will open doors for possible treatment modalities. Giving the patient a sense of control over their situation is critical for empowerment.

Opening questions that get this desired result might be:

- "Mrs. Jones, how can we help you?"
- "Mrs. Jones, what are your goals for your teeth, your mouth, and your smile?"
- "Mr. Smith, tell me what you like most about your teeth. What do you like least about your teeth?"
- "Mr. Smith, if there were anything you could change about your smile, what would that be?'

Once you ask a question, it is very important that you stop and listen. Repeat back to the person what you think you hear her saying, making sure you are hearing her clearly and accurately. Your listening skills are critical here. The patient will open her own doors. You must not close those doors by jumping in with your own dialogue. You want her to talk. You want her to give you information. You are looking for her emotional hot button—her motivator.

Critical to careful and caring listening is that you do not impose your own values on the person responding to your questions. As difficult as it may be at times, you must listen and accept a person's feelings even if they differ from your own. Asking questions, listening attentively, and not imposing your own values are not easy, but doing so will show respect for a person (Fig. 10-8).

Fig. 10-8: Initial Interview

- Learn how to ask questions and listen to a patient's ideas
- Be accepting of the differences expressed by each individual
- Determine a person's perceived or felt need
- Be ready to meet those needs

"Hank"

I have the privilege of consulting for a fabulous doctor, a former president of his state dental association. We had been studying case presentation, including the skill of listening. On this particular day, I was observing and evaluating one of his initial interviews.

This wonderful doctor performed one of the best initial interviews that I have ever observed. His patient was a 68-year-old woman. Her name was "Hank." She was a dapper woman, nicely dressed, hair combed, well groomed, and quite friendly.

During his initial interview, the doctor used great body language. He was seated on the same level with the patient, leaned slightly forward, and held steady, but comfortable eye contact with Hank during the entire interview. He told Hank that his clinical assistant was going to join them for the interview because he wanted her to take careful notes so that he could be fully attentive.

Once the social graces were completed, this doctor asked one of the best questions I have ever heard a doctor ask. He said, "Hank, tell me, what are your goals for your teeth, for your mouth and for your smile?" (I thought I would fall on the floor with that one! What a door opener!)

The following is Hank's response (notice the "motivators")

> "Well, Doctor, in two months I am going to my 50th high school reunion, and I want to look great. The teeth in the front of my mouth are all a different color, and I hate them. I want you to make them the same color. And on the bottom, I have 'gaposis' on both sides. I have one of those things that goes in and out, but I hate it. It hurts. I didn't even bring it today, because I just can't wear it. Do you do implants? And, Doctor, my husband died four years ago, and he went to his grave without his teeth. I don't want that to happen to me."

Hank's motivators were numerous:

- Time—she had two months
- Appearance—she didn't like the different colors on her front teeth. She wanted them to all be the same color. She wanted to look great!
- Comfort—her partial hurt her, and she couldn't wear it

KEYPOINT:

A person cannot be pushed into making a decision, but you can lead them into making a decision by asking the right questions.

• Function—Obviously, since she couldn't wear the partial, her chewing was being affected. She wanted something more permanent. She inquired about implants

• Keeping her teeth for a lifetime—she didn't want the same dental fate that her husband had endured

The only motivator that Hank did not mention was money. In fact, she didn't care about money. Money was not an issue for her. The power of the other motivators outweighed the issue of money. Remember: a person will buy what they want long before they will buy what they need.

Then the doctor recapped what Hank had said. "Let's see. Hank, you have a special event coming up, and you want us to see about getting your front teeth to match so you are happier with your smile. You want us to do something on the bottom so you are more comfortable and can chew better. You want us to help you get a healthy mouth so that you keep your teeth. Did I hear you right?"

Hank: "Yes, that's it."

Then the doctor asked the second best initial interview question that I have ever heard. He said, "Hank, tell me, what are your expectations of me?"

She said, "Well, doctor, I expect you to do the very best you can."

Now I am on the floor! Wow! What powerful questions. The first question opened the door for Hank to tell the doctor her needs as she saw them. She defined her own motivators so the doctor could be about the business of meeting those needs. Then the second question opened the door for Hank to give him permission to do the very best he could to reach those goals.

If you don't learn anything else from this book, learn the value of those two opening questions in your initial interview. By empowering the patient, she was telling him what to do rather than him telling her.

In addition, when a patient tells you what they want, and you respond to those wants, you are doing just what they have asked. If you tell them they need something, they may doubt it. But if they ask for it, they will buy it.

I didn't know the end of the story for a couple of months. Then, I was back in the office doing my next consult, and I asked about Hank. I said, "What ever happened to Hank? Did you get her fixed up?"

"Yes," they replied. "We did veneers on the top, restored the lower area, and have her on an excellent program of maintenance with our hygienist."

"Did you get it done in two months—before her reunion?"

"Oh, yes. See, Hank knew that she was going see her high school sweetheart at the reunion. They became reacquainted, fell in love again, and married. They kept both of their homes and go back and forth between two states and are doing great."

What a fun dental "love story" or human-interest story. You never know. And it all began with those awesome initial interview questions that opened the door for Hank to express her wants and needs. The patient received what she wanted, and the doctor was able to provide some great dental care and help a woman in need!

CLINICAL EVALUATION

Once the initial interview is completed and you are clear about the patient's goals, begin the clinical evaluation. The information gathered at the comprehensive oral evaluation becomes the worksheet for your treatment plan.

At the conclusion of this initial appointment, you will have established the following:

- The patient's perceived need and their self-determined personal goals
- The clinical need through careful and comprehensive diagnosis
- The groundwork for the treatment plan (Fig. 10-9)

After the necessary data have been gathered and the comprehensive evaluation has been concluded, invite the patient back to your practice for a consultation appointment. Find out who the decision-maker is and invite that person to the consultation appointment also. Tom Hopkins teaches "there is no reason to call for a decision if the decision-maker is not there."

For example:

Doctor: "Mrs. Jones, today we have gathered quite a bit of information about your situation. Now, I need to review the data and design a treatment plan that would help us to reach the goals that you outlined for me today. So, I would like to invite you back to the office in about a week so we can sit down together uninterrupted and discuss the treatment I believe would let us accomplish those goals. Would that be okay with you?"

Most people will be happy to come back for a consultation. They will be glad to have your undivided attention! You are going to be changing their smile. They will want to know what you are going to do and will want to be confident in the results you will achieve. Once they have agreed to return for a consultation, ask one last question.

Doctor: "Mrs. Jones, is there anyone besides yourself who will be deciding how you will proceed with treatment?"

Mrs. Jones: "Well, yes. For something like this, my husband and I decide together."

Doctor: "Your husband? Great. Then, let's schedule a consultation appointment that will work for the both of you. I think it is very important that he hears the recommendations that I will be making for your treatment. Would that be acceptable to you?"

You are trying to find out who the decision-maker might be. If there is someone who will be helping with that decision, try to make arrangements for that person to be at the consultation as well. Remember: there is no reason to call for a decision when the decision-maker is not there. You will be wasting your time and the patient's time. In addition, it may be impossible for a patient to go home and explain the treatment that you have recommended.

So, don't send a person home in hopes they can make a clear and precise presentation of your recommendations. Much will be lost in the translation!

Jameson management inc.

Treatment Plan

Patient's Name: _____ Date: _____

Home Phone: _____ Business Phone: _____

Date	Tooth Number	Service Needed	Phase	Time Between Appts.	Time Necessary	Fee	Appointment Time	Date

© Jameson management, Inc.

Fig. 10-9: Jameson Treatment Plan Form

Try to schedule the consultation within one week following the initial appointment. Don't make the mistake of letting too much time pass. Their interest may diminish.

Planning the case and your presentation

Between step 2 and 3 of the case presentation is the treatment-planning phase. Schedule time in your week for case planning. Plan your cases while the information is fresh in your mind. Plus, you will want to make sure that the case is carefully planned and organized before the patient returns for their consultation appointment. You, your team members, and your patient will benefit from the careful planning and documentation. Don't expect your team members to be able to make excellent financial arrangements or to schedule succinctly and accurately if they do not have thorough and appropriate information on the treatment plan. If the information is not carefully documented, they will have to guess or to interrupt you to get necessary information.

For the control of stress, the last thing in the world that you want is to walk in one morning only to have your business administrator or treatment coordinator say, "Doctor, Mrs. Jones is coming in at 10:00 A.M. for her treatment presentation. Is everything prepared?" and for you to hyperventilate because you haven't thought about the case since the patient came in for their initial appointment.

Be prepared. Give yourself permission to schedule time into your week for the planning of the cases. Pre-planning and careful preparation will pave the way for higher case acceptance.

Do not try to plan your case around what you think a person can afford. You plan the case, make a beautiful presentation of your recommendations, and then let your financial/treatment coordinator make the financial arrangements. The coordinator's responsibility will be to find a financial solution for the patient. Your responsibility is to design the best treatment plan possible so the patient is totally and comprehensively restored or has the most beautiful smile possible.

Your treatment plan (whether written manually or placed in the computer) should outline the following things:

- Specific treatment to be provided, including tooth number and surfaces where appropriate
- Order of treatment—where you want to start, how many teeth you would like to work on per appointment, where you want to go next, how many teeth you want to work on during that appointment, and so on throughout the mouth
- How much time you need for each appointment, including doctor time/ assistant time
- How much time you need between appointments, if appropriate
- The fee (to be completed by the financial coordinator)
- Date and time of the appointments, as they are scheduled

FIVE WAYS TO TURN BROCHURES INTO EDUCATIONAL TOOLS

Are your brochures hanging in a display on your wall in your reception area? Do patients read them often? Are they able to apply the information in the brochures to their own situation? Are your brochures powerful learning tools, or could they be doing more for you?

Educational brochures—when used properly—can be tremendous visual aids. They can be used to introduce dental concepts to your patients, to help you present your recommendations during the consultation appointment, and become great marketing tools.

Here are five suggestions of ways to turn your brochures into true teaching/visual aids.

1. Treatment Recommendations:

Visual aid presentations are most beneficial when certain methods of teaching are applied to their use. When you are discussing or recommending a particular treatment to a patient, pick up a relevant brochure and do the following:

- Select a brochure that shows a patient the end results of the treatment you are recommending.
- Open the brochure and with a pen or with a highlighter, accent the areas that are particularly relevant to that patient.
- Verbally inform the patient about how the brochure pertains to their situation. You might say something like:

> "Sarah, we have discussed your concern about the staining on your teeth. I have recommended a procedure called porcelain veneers. This brochure gives an explanation about this procedure—what is involved in the treatment and how the veneers look when treatment is completed. On this page you see that very little tooth preparation is necessary (highlight this) and that very little total time is involved in this treatment (highlight this). In two visits, we can remove those stains and produce that gorgeous smile you want."

- Close the brochure and write the person's name on the front and hand it to them. Then, continue.

> "Sarah, this brochure is for you. You can take it home so that you can reread it. I want you to fully understand the procedure and to know what's going to happen and what the end results of the treatment will mean for you. This brochure should answer most of the questions that you or your husband may have about porcelain veneers. But, please feel free to call about anything. We would love to help you get that new smile."

Instructing in this manner makes each person feel special. Handled in this manner, patients will be more likely to keep a brochure, read it again, and refer to it. This also gives them the opportunity to show a spouse or other family members the dentistry you have recommended. Decisions are often made jointly. Therefore, you benefit by extending your education to your patients' families as well.

2. Newsletters

In your patient education newsletter, include a colorful brochure about a particular procedure you are addressing in that issue. Example: The ADA brochure on periodontal disease, entitled "Gum Disease: The Eight Danger Signs," is a fantastic brochure. As you are educating your patients about periodontal disease, you will want to include articles about the subject in your newsletter, but the articles will be greatly enhanced and will have a far greater impact if a color brochure is included in that issue.

3. Informational Letters/Mailings

From time to time, you will want to mail special letters to your patient family telling them about a new procedure you are offering, informing them of a change in policy, making a special request of them, etc. You may have recently attended a course on a subject and want to inform and excite them about the new possibilities. In these letters, provide an informative brochure, which will provide further information and will serve as a visual aid.

4. Reception Area

It's fine to place or to display educational brochures in your reception area. Some people sitting in the reception area will pick up the brochures and read them. However, to encourage more reading of this literature, invite the patients to do just that! Don't assume that people will know that the brochures are theirs for the taking. Ask them to do so!

5. Continuous Care Notices

So many hygiene/continuous care notices carry a negative message such as: "You haven't been in to see us in _____ months! Where have you been?" and so on. Instead of a negative, naggy type of reminder or notification of their delinquent appointment, why not give them a wonderful reason to come in to the office! Invite these patients to come to the practice for their continuous care appointment and also to learn about the new techniques available in dentistry today. An educational brochure, included in these invitations, can stimulate curiosity and interest in new developments—such as porcelain veneers or bleaching. This type of invitation and brochure can motivate a person to phone for an appointment and can stimulate questions at the time of the appointment. Those people who are sitting on the fence may now have a reason to come in.

Brochures can be used effectively to promote your practice and to further educate people about the options available in dentistry today. Become a teacher of dentistry. Patients will gain from the new learning, and you will be able to provide more care. Increased education will lead to increased production.

Plan your presentation so that you can let the patient know the following three things:

- What is it? What are the features of this treatment? Remember: people don't know what you are talking about. You must show them
- What are the benefits and end results of the treatment? Focus your benefit statements around their particular wants and needs. Remember: people want to know "what's in this for me?"
- Can you do this? Can you get the results the patient wants? Provide proof. At this point, your before and after photographs or intra-oral camera images will prove invaluable (Fig. 10-10)

Every person on the team should look at every patient as if they are totally and completely restored. Comprehensive diagnosis and treatment planning, followed by a well-orchestrated case presentation, get everyone focused on that goal, including the patients.

Fig. 10-10: Video Dentistry

Education is your biggest commission.

Consider having the financial/treatment co-ordinator join you while you are planning the case. It will be beneficial for him or her to hear what you want to do, how you want to do it, and why. The third-party backup support of you and of the case will be invaluable. Many patients will ask the coordinator questions that they won't ask the doctor. Rather than have to leave the patient to get up and go ask a question or to look uninformed, make sure the coordinator is as carefully prepared as the doctor.

Do this: ask your financial/treatment coordinator if he or she would like to know about the case before the presentation takes place. The answer will be an overwhelming "Yes!" The coordinator wants to be organized. Let him or her be just that. Having been informed, the financial/treatment coordinator will be more productive and will be relieved of a great deal of stress.

Step 3: Educate and Motivate

Step 3 of a case presentation is to educate and motivate the patient. As dental care providers, you are educators of dentistry. People don't come to the dental office with very much dental knowledge. In fact, the number one reason people don't come to the dentist or do not say "yes" to the recommended

KEYPOINT:

Approximately 83%
of a person's learning
takes place visually.

KEYPOINT:

A confused person
cannot make
a decision

treatment is that there is no perceived need or there is a lack of dental education.

Education and motivation are critical parts of the consultation. The consultation appointment is the time when patients come to spend quality time with you to review your findings, to hear your recommendations, and to find out what you can do for them.

The consultation appointment was scheduled at the end of the initial appointment. You have spent some time carefully designing a treatment plan. In addition, you have spent time planning your presentation. Your consultation is your opportunity to present. It is at this time that most people will decide whether they are going to proceed or not. This is a critical time in your interaction with your patient and, perhaps, with the decision-maker. At the consultation appointment, everything in the consultation area is prepared prior to the patient's arrival.

As educators, you must access the best methods of teaching. Approximately 83% of a person's learning takes place visually.

This is the main mode of learning for most people. Therefore, it makes sense to access excellent visual aids.

Keep your presentation focused on end results and refrain from technical jargon. Often, dental professionals get so involved with describing the clinical technique of treatment that they totally lose the patients. The patient becomes confused.

Use layman's language. Access excellent visual aids such as beautiful "before and after" photographs of your dentistry to let a person visualize what you are explaining.

Develop your own photo album. Develop a library of before and after photography on your intra-oral camera. Imaging is, of course, a tremendous asset if such technology is available. Patient education videos are available as well as slide presentations. Brochures showing the options available in your practice are effective if properly managed. Search for the visual aids that fit your practice and you. Then use these aids to individualize your instruction (Fig. 10-11).

Fig. 10-11: Imaging Software

VIDEO DENTISTRY

Use of visual aids places a person in a comfort zone that is conducive to learning. This comfort level opens the doors to a two-way line of constructive communication. Use of an intra-oral or digital camera and/or an imaging system enhances communication. When a person can see the possibilities for their own smile, motivation increases significantly. Consider the benefits of video dentistry.

Intra-oral and/or digital cameras

Include taking a tour of the mouth with an intra-oral and/or digital camera in each new patient appointment. Determine the photographs you are going to take, and do so on all patients. For example:

- Full face, smiling. No lip retractors. Capture the lip line for your laboratory
- Smile with lip retractors
- Right and left lateral with lip retractors
- All 4 quadrants (take photographs of individual teeth within each quadrant where a tooth indicates a need)
- Upper and lower arch

Look at both the upper and lower anteriors. Let the patient focus on the upper anteriors and ask, "What do you like most about the teeth in the front of your mouth—on the top? What do you like least? If you could change anything about the teeth here, what would you change?"

Then, go to the lower anteriors, and so on. Let patients begin to see their teeth in a new way. Let them tell you what they want.

Either store these images or run prints. You will want to use these images during your consultation appointment.

Use the intra oral and/or digital camera photographs as a way to communicate with your ceramic specialist. When the ceramic specialists from your laboratory can actually see the situation and discuss the case with you, they will be much better able to achieve the desired result in the preparations. You would have a visual prescription, as well as a written one.

Develop a library of before and after intra-oral and/or digital camera photographs. Take before and after photos of every case. Then, as you are planning your cases and presentations, you will be able to use these before and after photos to show similar situations to patients who are considering treatment. For example: seeing the features of porcelain laminate veneers, realizing the benefits of this type of treatment, and obtaining proof that you can access results are powerful in your presentations.

Consider using these cameras on your regular patients who may be coming to the practice for a hygienic appointment. Give the patients the smile evaluation. Then, if a door to any cosmetic possibility has been opened, take the opportunity to do a tour of the mouth.

Please do not hesitate to schedule additional time into your hygiene appointments, if you choose to include the intra-oral and/or digital camera in many of these vital appointments. Your hygienist is an excellent educator. He/she can open all kinds of doors for restorative and/or cosmetic opportunities. However, there must be scheduled time to do this. The time will be well spent and will pay for itself multifold if patients begin to accept treatment as a result of the dental education.

Imaging software

Imaging software is becoming more and more popular. These are easily integrated into most practice management software today. With the use of imaging, you can take a photograph of a patient's existing smile and digitally change the smile. Once you and the patient agree on the plan of action to create the desired smile, you can send this image to the laboratory to further enhance your prescription. You can send the proposed smile makeover home with the patient for contemplation and discussion with family members. You can enhance your educational and motivational presentation to the patient about the smile change.

As is true with any system in a practice, comprehensive understanding and use the imaging software by the entire team is necessary to ensure its productivity and profitability. "An intra-oral camera or a cosmetic imaging system is not just an investment in money," says Dr. Larry Rosenthal of Manhattan, NY. "It is also an investment in time. But it works! The excitement it will generate for the doctor, for the staff, and for the patients is unparalleled."

Knowing this vital information lets you gear your presentation toward the patient's perceived needs.

Get in focus with the patient

At your initial interview, you established the person's emotional hot buttons or main motivators:

- appearance
- comfort
- function
- keeping the teeth for a lifetime

- time
- money

As I have said before, a person will buy what is wanted long before buying what is needed. So, get on his/her side. You will get a great deal further with treatment acceptance if both you and the patient are after the same thing. People want to know, "How is this going to affect me? What is in this for me? How is this going to affect my health, my looks, my pocketbook, my schedule?" Determine their main motivator or motivators. Direct your comments and your presentation accordingly.

For example: During the initial interview you may have asked the question:

Doctor: "Mrs. Jones, tell me, if there was anything that you could change about your smile, what would that be?"

Patient: "Well, I just hate my teeth. They have stains all over them, and I'm embarrassed to open my mouth. I usually just cover my mouth when I smile or laugh, and I am really ready to change that."

Doctor: "You're unhappy with the discoloration of your teeth, and you are interested in getting a whiter, brighter smile. Is that right?"

Patient: "Yes!"

You know that this person's main motivational factor is appearance. When she comes back to the office for consultation, have your visual aids, appropriate books, brochures, or images on your intra-oral camera readily available. Your presentation should be simple, direct, and geared toward answering that patient's perceived need.

For example:

Doctor: "Mrs. Jones, last week when you were here for your initial appointment, you indicated a concern about the color of your teeth. Let me show you a picture of a person who had a situation similar to yours. She had stained teeth also. Can you see the similarity?"

Patient: "Yes. That looks just like my teeth."

Doctor: "Once we completed her treatment, she looked like this. (Switch to the after image.) What do you think?"

Patient: "That's great."

Doctor: "Well, Mrs. Jones, I am comfortable telling you that once we complete your treatment, your smile will look similar to this. Would this be of interest to you?"

She will probably say "yes." Then, go into some detail about the treatment recommendation, but don't go into incredible detail on the technique itself.

Keep the presentation short! No more than 20 minutes of doctor time (and that may be too long in some situations). A person's attention span in this environment is approximately 17 minutes, so keep the presentation short, to the point, visual, and motivational. If you use an intra-oral camera to show a person what is going on in their own mouth and to show the person before and after photos of similar situations, your case presentation will not only be more effective, it will go much more quickly.

The importance of clear organization

- Be well prepared in advance of the patient's arrival—the treatment plan, the financial data, the visual aids, and the organization of your presentation. Know what you are going to do and say
- After brief social graces, get to the point. Don't take too long before you address the business at hand

- Only include information that the patient needs. Don't include irrelevant information (like too much clinical data)
- On the other hand, don't leave out necessary information. Be sure to focus on the patient's motivational hot button. You ascertained that critical insight during your initial interview. If questions arise during your presentation, listen. Take a note and make sure that you address the question when the time is appropriate
- Present your recommendations in a clear, logical order. Don't forget that the patient knows little about dentistry. Your careful presentation must lead him/her to a point where a decision can be made.
- Present to the emotion and back up your presentation with logic. Lead with the need, not with your product or service

Here are the steps to follow during your presentation:

- What does the patient have now?
- What treatment do you recommend to restore his/her mouth to health again or to create that beautiful smile?
- What are the advantages or benefits of proceeding with treatment?
- What are the disadvantages of not proceeding with treatment?

After you have explained your presentation, go to step 4 (Fig. 10-12).

Step 4: Ask for the Commitment

Step 4 in a case presentation is to ask for a commitment. Dental teams often fall short here. They are a little bit uncomfortable asking for a commitment or closing! You must ask for a commitment, or you will have a lot of people walking out the door, and you will not know if they are going ahead with treatment or not.

Asking for a commitment means getting comfortable asking questions that will either confirm a person's desire to proceed with treatment or pinpoint any barriers to treatment acceptance. In order to get comfortable with this aspect of case presentation, practice or role-play various situations as a team. The only way you will get comfortable asking closing questions is to practice until they become second nature to you. Then use them. Once you see the effectiveness of these questions, you will continue without exception.

Fig. 10-12: Case Presentation

I have so many doctors tell me that they will be mowing the lawn, watching TV, or sleeping, and all of a sudden will wonder, "What ever happened to Mrs. Jones? I wonder if she scheduled an appointment? I wonder if she is going ahead with treatment. I have to remember to ask Susie about her tomorrow." Then they stew about the patient. This is a stress point deluxe! You must become comfortable asking for this commitment for two reasons: to find out if the person is going ahead or not, and to uncover any barriers to treatment acceptance. Otherwise, non-acceptance will result much too often.

Examples of closing questions

Doctor: "Mrs. Jones, have I explained the treatment so that you are comfortable with my explanation?"

Patient: "Yes, I'm clear on what needs to be done."

Doctor: "Then do you have any further questions about the treatment?"

Patient: "Well, no, I guess not."

Doctor: "Then shall we go ahead and schedule an appointment to begin your treatment?"

Patient: "I see no problems. Let's go ahead."

Doctor: "Okay. I am going to have Jan, my treatment coordinator, discuss the financial responsibilities, and then she will schedule your first appointment. I look forward to working with you."

Other examples of closing questions are as follows:

- Is this the type of treatment you would like to receive?
- Is there any reason why we shouldn't schedule an appointment to begin your treatment?
- If we can change your smile and have you looking similar to this, would that work for you?
- Keeping your teeth for a lifetime is an important goal for you, am I right? Then, working together to make sure that happens is also important. So, when would you like to begin to get and maintain your oral health?
- Would having a smile such as the ones we have just reviewed make you happy? Then, let's get started. Are mornings or afternoons better for you?
- Do you need more information, or have I given you enough information for you to make your decision?
- Do you agree that this type of treatment would let you restore your mouth to health again? When would you like to start getting healthier?
- Is this the type of treatment you feel would benefit you?
- Would what I am proposing fit into your goals?
- Are we in agreement that this treatment proposal would serve as a solution to your problem (or to your interest in changing your smile)?

By asking a closing question, you are trying to determine if the person is ready to proceed or if there are any barriers to treatment acceptance. As stated previously, a good management principle is this: "A problem is only a problem until it becomes defined. Once it becomes defined, it becomes manageable." Unless you find out what the barriers to treatment acceptance are, you don't have a chance to clear the way. This gives you an amazing opportunity. Once you know what the barrier is, you can begin to work on problem-solving! The proven method of problem-solving, discussed in Chapter 7, is appropriate here. This excellent method of communication will make a profound difference in your productivity. The only way to discover the objections or barriers to acceptance is to ask questions.

Here are four key principles to know about objections:

- The way to identify an objection is to ask questions
- An objection is a request for further information indicating that the person is interested in your proposal
- If a person doesn't present an objection, that probably means that he/she isn't interested
- Objections are the steps necessary to the close

So, I hope that from this day forward, you will see objections in a whole new light. An objection is a gift! If a person presents an objection, he/she is interested in your proposal and is looking to you for help in finding a solution.

We will study the handling of objections more thoroughly in the next chapter.

Once the closing question has been asked and there are no more clinical questions, the doctor excuses himself or herself, and the treatment coordinator or financial coordinator takes over.

If at any time during the initial interview, the comprehensive evaluation or the case presentation a patient asks, "How much is this going to cost?" answer this question with a question. Make sure that you are hearing what is being asked both clearly and accurately. In addition, make sure to keep the money questions where they need to be.

If you quote a fee before the person has made a mental decision that treatment is wanted, he/she will hear nothing of your explanation. His/her mind will be overwhelmed with thoughts of money, and will miss your entire presentation.

So, if a patient asks you a money question before you are ready to field those types of questions, answer in the following way:

Doctor: "Mrs. Jones, are you concerned about the financing of your treatment?"

Ms. Jones: "Yes. I just don't know how much this is going to cost, and I don't know if I can afford it."

Doctor: "I can certainly appreciate your concerns. I am going to have Jan, my treatment coordinator, discuss the total fee and the options we have available for payment. She is very experienced and is excellent. I am sure she will be able to work this out with you.

Once we have determined how we will proceed with treatment, Jan will discuss all fee questions with you. However, for now, Mrs. Jones, I would like to present to you my recommendations—the treatment that I believe would help you accomplish the goals you outlined for me last week. However, know that you are in total control here. You get to say if you want to proceed or not. Please know that we will discuss all financial matters in full before we begin. So, for right now, my responsibility is to show you what I believe would be the very best treatment possible. Would that be alright with you?"

In this example, the doctor acknowledged the patient's concern (her objection), but did not start quoting fees. If you begin quoting fees at this point, before the patient has "bought into" the treatment, you risk getting so involved with the financial aspects of the case that you never get to the treatment. I don't have a problem with the doctor quoting the fee, but I prefer that a financial coordinator/treatment coordinator make all financial arrangements. However, make an effort to keep the money questions in a constructive place within your presentation.

All clinical questions must be answered before a discussion of money takes place. Once all clinical questions have been answered, and the person indicates a desire to go ahead with treatment, proceed with steps 5 and 6: Making financial arrangements and scheduling the first appointment, respectively (Fig. 10-13).

Fig. 10-13: Financial Arrangements

KEYPOINT:

Financial arrangements
always precede
the scheduling
of an appointment.

In Summary

The following are the six steps of case presentation/treatment acceptance:

- Build the relationship
- Establish the need
- Educate and motivate
- Ask for a commitment
- Make financial arrangements
- Schedule an appointment

Follow this proven six-step process, and you will find that your acceptance rate will increase significantly. The keys to this are building the relationship and helping the person feel involved in the decision-making process.

Involve your patients in case presentation by asking questions and finding out what they want or need. Respond to their wants and needs. Organize your presentation. Success requires preparedness. Use visual aids to more successfully educate. Ask for the commitment. Ask questions to find out what the barriers to acceptance might be. Patients then have a chance to tell you

KEYPOINT:

"Tell me and I will forget. Show me and I might remember. Involve me and I will understand."

–Chinese proverb

about barriers that are getting in the way. Then you have a chance to clear those barriers.

This method of case presentation is a two-way communication between you and the patient. Both parties benefit—the patient receives wanted and needed dental treatment, and your team gets the opportunity to perform great dentistry. Everyone wins! That's dental teamwork!

11

HANDLING OBJECTIONS

I am not judged by the number of times I fail,
but by the number of times I succeed, and the number
of times I succeed is in direct proportion to the number
of times I can fail and keep trying.

— TOM HOPKINS

*I*n Chapter 10, I encouraged you to ask for a commitment to find out if the patient is ready to move ahead with treatment or if there are any barriers or objections that need to be addressed. Let me reinforce the truism that unless an objection is identified and addressed, the likelihood of a person going ahead with treatment is slim. In addition, if a person goes ahead with treatment, but there is an objection that has not been solved, problems may surface somewhere down the line.

The question then is "How do you define the objections, and then how do you deal effectively with them?"

Remember from Chapter 10 the four key principles to know about objections:

- The way to identify an objection is to ask questions
- An objection is a request for further information, indicating that the person is interested in your proposal
- If a person doesn't present an objection, that probably means he/she isn't interested
- Objections are the steps necessary to the close

HANDLING OBJECTIONS

Tom Hopkins of Scottsdale, Arizona, is considered one of the best sales trainers in the world. As a student of Mr. Hopkins, I have learned the valuable skills of identifying and handling objections. I cannot think of anything that has been more beneficial to me in my professional and personal life.

Objections, barriers, or problems are going to happen to everyone— probably every day. Success in any relationship and in any business will depend on your ability to effectively deal with these realities.

STEPS TO OVERCOME OBJECTIONS

When a patient poses an objection, take the following steps:

1. Hear out the objection

Don't interrupt. Encourage the person to express himself or herself. Objections often diminish when a person is allowed to talk about it. In addition, this gives you another chance to listen, to show concern, to empathize (not sympathize), and to let the person sense your understanding. Thus, you validate your patient!

Let the person tell you everything. Hear the person out. Let him/her tell you as much as possible. Information is power. The more he/she tells you, the better chance you will have to solve the problem. Don't become defensive. This will only cause the other person to get defensive, and you will go nowhere. If someone has a problem, don't take it personally. More than likely, he/she is upset with the situation, not with you.

Ask questions. Use listening body language. Passively listen to encourage him/her to go on. Then, actively listen.

2. Actively listen

Rephrase and reflect back to the person what you think you have heard him/her say. This gives you a chance to:

- clarify
- reinforce the patient
- move forward

Pay attention to the feelings being expressed and the behavior that is causing the person to feel that way. This gives you a chance to clarify. Are you hearing him/her accurately? In addition, if the person is angry or upset, active listening will prove to be a calming agent. You will help to "deflood." It is vital in this situation that you help the objecting patient to regain a balance between emotion and logic. Then, and only then, can a reasonable discussion take place.

3. Reinforce the importance of the objection

There's no benefit to disagreeing or arguing with a patient. When you listen to the concerns, express an understanding of those concerns. Share in the development of possible solutions. If you can accurately determine what the objection is without irritating the person, you will be in a position to generate possible ideas for a solution. That's what you want—a solution to the problem. If an acceptable solution can be developed, you will be more likely to see that patient leave with a scheduled appointment.

For example:

Patient: "I don't want to lose my teeth, but I sure don't want to spend this much money if this isn't going to last."

Doctor: "Keeping your teeth for a lifetime is important to you, and you want to make sure that the investment you make is going to be one that lasts for as long as possible, is that right?"

Patient: "Yes."

Doctor: "I totally agree with you. That's what we want for you."

Answer the objection. Provide further education. Turn the objection into a benefit. Establish value. Use the "**feel, felt, found**" response:

Doctor: "Mr. Patient, I understand how you feel. Many patients have felt the same concern about making an investment in comprehensive dental care until they found out that an investment in quality, comprehensive care now will:

- provide better health
- last longer
- look better
- save money in the long run"

4. Offer a solution to the problem

Give the patient a possible solution to the question. More than likely, if you have listened carefully, you will be able to offer solutions that will resolve the issue.

Patient: "I don't know about this. I'm not sure I can afford this. Is there any way I can pay this out?"

Doctor: "We do have several financial options available, and I'm sure one will work well for you. We have options that will let you stretch your payments over a long period of time. How much per month would be comfortable for you?"

Or:

Doctor: "This type of comprehensive care, provided now, would answer your concern about making a stable, long term investment, wouldn't it?"

5. Check to see if the solution will work for the patient

If the solution answers the question and solves the problem, then you are well on your way.

Doctor: "If we are able to make the financing of the dentistry comfortable for you, is this the type of treatment you would like to receive?"

If the answer is "yes," then proceed to the next step.

6. Change the direction of the conversation—move forward

Once you have answered the objection, change the flow or focus of the conversation. Move to another area of interest that will move the conversation in a positive direction.

Doctor: "I was wondering, Mr. Patient, do you have any particular scheduling concerns that we need to be aware of?"

7. Close

Once you have dealt with the objections, ask for a commitment, or "close." Closing an agreement means asking!

Doctor: "Mrs. Jones, is there anything else that would keep us from going ahead with your treatment, or are you ready to schedule that first appointment?"

Here are the steps to handling objections:

- Hear out the objection
- Actively listen
- Reinforce the importance of the objection
- Offer a solution to the problem

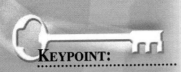

- Check to see if the solution will work for the patient
- Change the direction of the conversation— move forward
- Close

Remember that you stay in control of a conversation by asking carefully engineered questions leading the conversation in the direction you want to go. When a person poses an objection, don't freeze up and feel that you have hit a dead end. Not so!

THE NON-COMPLYING PATIENT

The non-complying patient—they are full of objections! Oh, what energy one must exude to deal with these folks! Do any of the following situations produce stress in your life?

- Knowing what a person needs, but not being able to lead him/her to a decision to go ahead
- Knowing the dentistry is there, but not being able to turn treatment plans into treatment realities
- Having a patient who does not follow through with preventive home care measures or with necessary co-therapy
- Dealing with patients who break appointments or who "no show"

Can competency in communication skills help in these situations? Can communication skills be an asset to acquiring case acceptance or treatment completion, cooperation with home care, or co-therapy? Can your ability to communicate effectively have an effect on your bottom line? Can communication expertise help control the stress caused by non-compliance? Yes!

My husband, John, believes that the non-complying patient has been one of his greatest sources of stress over his years of practice. He states:

> *I have found that I become frustrated when I cannot communicate the need for the treatment well enough to motivate patients to prioritize dental care in their lives. If I'm not able to establish the need; if I'm not able to create the 'want to,' then obstacles and barriers such as finances get in the way of a person saying 'yes' to my recommendations.*

> *My feeling of self-worth and my confidence suffered until I realized that I needed to learn and improve my communication skills, and that these communication skills were going to be the key to getting my message across effectively. I had the clinical skills! I wanted to provide the care! But, I needed the communication skills to pull it all together.*

> *Now, more patients are receiving more care. They're happy and so am I.*

Let's look at some stressful situations and apply the communication skills we have learned so far to gain better control of these situations.

You, as the dentist, know what a person needs in his/her mouth to accomplish excellent oral health and an attractive smile. Frustration comes when you see what a patient needs, and you can't encourage him/her to go ahead.

Many times the treatment recommendations are explained, the doctor or treatment coordinator asks if there are any questions, the patient says "no," and that is that. There is no asking for the commitment. Then doctors wonder, "What happened to Mrs. Jones? Did she schedule an appointment? She didn't? I wonder why?"

Find out "why" before Mrs. Jones leaves the consultation appointment. If she is not going to comply with recommendations, uncover the objections or barriers before she leaves the office. Only then will you have the opportunity to resolve or "de-fuse" barriers to treatment acceptance.

How can you do that? How can you find out why?

Once treatment recommendations have been presented, it is appropriate to ask if there are any questions. But control those questions. First find if there is any confusion about the treatment itself. Then begin your search for barriers.

For example:

Doctor: "Mrs. Jones, have I explained my treatment recommendations so that you are comfortable with my explanation?"

Or:

Doctor: "Mrs. Jones, do you have any questions about the treatment itself?"

These questions focus the patient on the treatment and on questions about that treatment. You will want to deal with technical questions before entering into a discussion of potential obstacles such as finances.

These questions also place the responsibility of the explanation right where it belongs and that is on the teacher—the doctor or the treatment coordinator. You are responsible for the explanation. The patient is not responsible for the understanding. You are the teacher.

Once any confusion or questions are cleared, the next step is to investigate possible objections.

You will be asking for a commitment to proceed with treatment, and you will be trying to isolate barriers at the same time. If you never know what the barrier to treatment acceptance is, you will never have a chance to overcome that barrier.

OVERCOMING OBJECTIONS

There are four main reasons why people either don't go to the dentist at all or why they don't comply with your treatment or prevention recommendations. These four major objections are:

1. no perceived need—lack of dental education
2. fear of cost
3. fear of the dentistry itself
4. time

If you can constructively deal with or overcome these four objections, your number of new patients will increase and your number of non-complying patients will decrease.

Tom Hopkins says there are four Ps of professionalism. He says that it takes all four of these to master any skill. Overcoming or handling objections is one of the skills that is essential to your practice productivity, and it is one that will require the four "Ps." These four "Ps" of professionalism are as follows:

- Preplan
- Practice
- Perfect
- Perform

As a team, do the following:

Preplan

- Discuss each of the four reasons people do not accept treatment, citing specific examples of each
- Plan how you will try to overcome those objections
- Write verbal scripts for handling those issues

Practice

- Practice those scripts with each other—role play—get comfortable
- Practice the skills as patients flow through the office and as objections are presented

Perfect

- Perfect your skills—evaluate various situations
- Write down and/or discuss what went well and what didn't
- If something is working well for you, stress this point to the other team members—do more to build on these positives

- If something is not working well for you, change it!—redo, rewrite, replan your course of action—but don't throw in the towel if your first plan doesn't work!—persevere

Perform

- Continue to work on your presentations even during that tough period of change
- Don't fall back into your old ways—continue to move forward and get better

LISTEN ACCURATELY

Remember active listening? When a person poses an objection, reflect to the person what you think you've heard, making sure that you are hearing correctly. This type of listening is critical if the objection is to be identified and overcome.

By actively listening or responding reflectively, you accomplish the following:

- Establish empathy
- Express a warm and caring attitude
- Show respect
- Defuse fear or anger
- Move the conversation forward

Ultimately, you stay in control of a conversation by asking questions and then accurately listening.

Here are suggested communication/verbal skills for dealing with these four main reasons for non-compliance or the four major objections in dentistry—notice the use of questions and active listening.

Situation One: No perceived need/lack of dental education

For example: A patient is informed of the presence of decay following a continuous care appointment.

Ms. Patient: "I'm sick of hearing that I have decay every time I come in for a cleaning."

Hygienist: "You're bothered by the fact that we find decay at most of your visits."

Ms. Patient:: "Yes! I'd love to come to have my teeth cleaned and have you say "no cavities!"

Hygienist: "I'm confused. You say you'd like those "no cavity" appointments, but the status of your mouth shows that your home care is not regular. Are you saying that in order to become healthier and to prevent the decay, you would become more committed to a co-therapy regime?"

Softly, but effectively, the hygienist identifies a discrepancy in the patient's values. Then the patient is given the chance to decide if she wants to make the necessary changes. If she makes an affirmative decision, she will be more likely to stick to it than if the hygienist decides for her. Lead the patient to making decisions that are positive. Lead with questions.

Situation Two: Fear of cost

Patient: "Gee, I didn't think this would cost this much. I just don't think I can afford this right now."

It's frustrating when you have identified a patient's perceived and clinical needs, have presented the case excellently, understood clearly from the patient that this is the type of care they would like to receive, and yet they walk out the door saying, "I just can't afford it."

Even though you can understand and empathize with the patient, this is a major frustration. In addition, too many of these kinds of responses will make the entire team "gun shy." They will begin thinking, even before you present the case, that a person won't be able to afford it, so you compromise the treatment plan or just do a tooth at a time. Often, a team gets in its own way by prejudging a person's desire to receive the care or ability to pay. So, to work at overcoming the 'fear of cost' barrier, consider the following:

KEYPOINT:

*Your entire team
must believe
in the services
you are providing.*

Validate the quality of your services to yourselves. Do you feel that the value of your services exceeds the fee you are asking for that service? Before anything else happens, you must convince yourself of your own worth! The confidence that you and every member of the team has in the quality and benefit of the recommended treatment is of central importance to overcoming the fear of cost.

Everyone must have a strong commitment to your work and to the patients you serve. You, as dental professionals, add value to the lives of those people. Be constantly clear about the mission and purpose of your practice (see Chapter 2). If you do not already have a written mission statement, I encourage you to have a team meeting in which you discuss the following:

- Who you are
- What you are about
- What you intend to accomplish in your practice

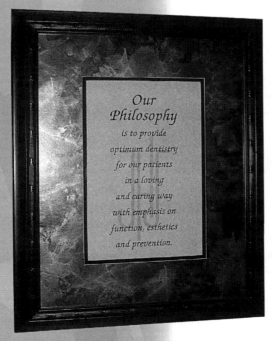

*Our
Philosophy
is to provide
optimum dentistry
for our patients
in a loving
and caring way
with emphasis on
function, esthetics
and prevention.*

The statement of mission must be empowered by emotional words that are motivational to you. Everyone should be in agreement that the statement says it all. The statement should be short and to the point, but powerful in its message. Have the message printed, matted, and framed. Hang it where everyone can see it on a regular basis (Fig. 11-1).

As you write your goals for your practice, ask yourself this question: "If we accomplish this goal, will it bring us closer to

Fig. 11-1: Mission Statement

satisfying our ultimate mission?" If the answer is "yes," then you probably have a good goal. Go for it!

EXERCISE

List the services you provide for your patients from the initial contact through the entire treatment.

- What makes your services special?
- What "added value" touches do you provide that make your practice unique?
- What do you do that goes beyond the expected?

KEYPOINT:

You must establish a relationship of trust and confidence with a patient before treatment acceptance will result.

Make sure that the treatment your patients are receiving is an equitable exchange for the fee. Thus, VALUE = VALUE.

Do this exercise as a team. This will help you to see in your own hearts and minds the things that you are presently doing in which you go above and beyond the call of duty. This will make you see the value of your services and will help you deal with the issue of cost. Remember: validating the fee for the services in the minds and hearts of all team members is the first step to overcoming the fear of cost in your patients.

Validate yourself personally to your patients. Patients must know that they can count on you and

can receive the same type of treatment and care every time they are in your practice. Consistency of care is critical to establishing the trust that is foundational to treatment acceptance. Your on-going internal marketing program or public relations program should have this as its foundation.

In planning your marketing/educational program, ask this question: "Does this marketing tool make a statement (consciously or subconsciously) about who we are, what we do, and what our purpose is about?"

If the answer is "yes," then the marketing tool is probably going to serve your purpose well. If the answer is "no," then you may need to rethink the project.

Validate your services. In your efforts to validate your services to existing and potential clients, do the following to let patients know the following three things:

- *Description/explanation*—what it is you are recommending? For example, what is a bridge?
- *Advantages*—what are the benefits of this procedure? (How will this help the patient?)
- *Proof*—can you produce the results?

  - Use testimonial letters from enthusiastic patients
  - Use before and after photographs of your patients to illustrate a particular service you provide (Be sure to obtain written permission from your patients before you use their photographs)
  - Provide civic presentations throughout your community using before and after

slides of treatment you have provided. Of course, this presentation should be non-self serving. It would be an educational program letting people in your area know what kind of services are available to them in dentistry today. Tremendous credibility can result

- Intra-oral or digital cameras. Use of an intra-oral or digital camera to show a person what they have in their mouth presently validates your recommendations more than anything else. When people can see the evidence themselves, they will see the needs immediately (Fig. 11-2)

KEYPOINT:

You want to have the exchange of value be one of equitability but one that is perceived to tilt in the favor of the patient.

Fig. 11-2: Intra-oral or Digital cameras as Presentation Tools

Validate your practice. Make sure that every aspect of your practice epitomizes the professional image you wish to project.

Be committed to comprehensive quality in every fiber of your practice. Make sure that everything in your practice consistently sends a message of excellence to your patients—the telephone conversations, the facility, the written communication, the actual treatment, the management situations, each and every team member, etc. Evaluate. Be honest with yourselves. What says quality? What doesn't?

Drive to your own office. Put on your "patient eyes." What impression do you get? Does every step of the patient visit invite trust and confidence? Does everything speak of quality? Are the patients going to get the impression that you will take good care of them by the kind of care you give your facility? Is the team focused on one thing—the care of the patients? Does that come across loud and clear?

EXERCISE

1. List the main financial barriers or objections your patients give to you.
2. Using the skills from this chapter, formulate scripts that will help you deal with and overcome these objections.
3. Role-play using these scripts.
4. After the role playing, answer these questions:
   a. Did I listen carefully?
   b. Did I reflect what I thought were the patients' main concerns?
   c. Did I validate the patient?
   d. Did I answer each objection with a "values" question?
   e. Did I go through the steps of dealing with an objection?
   f. When did I overcome the objections? Did I close?

Situation Three: Fear of the dentistry itself

Example: A patient is presented with ideal dentistry, but her dental fear is getting in the way of her going ahead with the treatment of choice.

Ms. Patient: "Root canal! No way! I've heard about those things! I just want you to pull that tooth out."

Doctor: "Sounds like you're apprehensive about the treatment I've recommended for you."

Ms. Patient "That's putting it mildly! I don't want to lose that tooth, but I don't think I could handle a root canal."

(Use the "feel, felt, found" here, along with great visual aids to educate.)

Doctor: "I understand how you *feel*, Ms. Patient. Many of our patients have *felt* the same way, until they *found* out that we are committed to comfortable dentistry here, and we will make sure your treatment is as short as possible and as comfortable. Since you want to save the tooth, and since we *can* do this in a timely and comfortable manner, is there any other reason why we should not go ahead with your treatment?"

The doctor didn't impose a value judgment on the patient, such as: "That's silly! I can't believe you want to have this tooth extracted."

Or:

"There's no reason to be nervous/scared/worried about a root canal!"

It does no good to tell a person not to be afraid. If they are, they are! Acknowledge the fear. Validate their emotions. Please remember that the single best way to help a person defuse fear is to actively listen. Then, make effort to educate, resolve the fear, and build confidence. You'll find that your warmth and empathy will take you a great deal further. If you can deal positively with the fear of the dentistry, you'll have many more patients comply, fewer broken appointments, and fewer no shows.

In his book, *Helping and Human Relations: A Primer For Lay and Professional Helpers*, R.R. Carkhuff points out that professionals who communicate with a high degree of warmth, caring, and empathy are reported by patients to be more effective in social, personal, and vocational functioning. This type of "facilitative communication" makes it easier for people to openly discuss problems, express feelings related to a situation, and make decisions about treatment. In other words, compliance and cooperation are advanced.

Situation Four: Time

Example: It's not convenient for a patient to schedule appointments, keep appointments, or commit to full, comprehensive treatment because of time constraints.

Appointment Coordinator: "Mr. Patient, we reserve specific times of the day for this type of intricate and detailed procedure. In order for the doctor and the clinical team to give the necessary attention to you, we need to reserve special time. Tell me, are mornings or afternoons best for you?"

Mr. Patient: "Mornings are best, but I don't know if I can be here next week. Can I just call you when I can come in."

Appointment Coordinator: "Next week is a problem for you?"

Mr. Patient:: "Yes. I have meetings all week, and I just don't think you could count on me."

Appointment Coordinator: "Well, I appreciate your honesty. I don't want to reserve this time for Dr. Jameson without being sure you will be here! Does the week after look better for you?"

Mr. Patient: "I just don't know. I'll just call you."

Appointment Coordinator: "Mr. Patient, let me make a note to myself that you do wish to proceed with this treatment, but that time is a concern for you. With your permission, I will call you in a couple of weeks to schedule the first appointment. Would that be okay with you?"

Mr. Patient: "Sure."

The appointment coordinator remained in control of the conversation and of the appointment book by asking the patient's permission to call him. When you let patients say that they are is going to "call you," you turn the controls over to them.

In this type of situation where the patient is difficult to schedule or cannot be counted on to keep appointments, it is vital that you do the following:

- Maintain control of the situation
- Set the tone for the appointment by stressing:

    - the importance of the appointment
    - that you reserve special time for them
    - that because they are special, you want to give them your best care and offer appointment times that are best for them as well as for the doctor/hygienist

- Offer alternatives of choice. Offer two choices, no more. Either answer must be okay with you (*e.g.*, mornings or afternoons)
- Place the responsibility of the appointment on the shoulders of the patient
- Ask permission to call a patient rather than letting him/her call you. Often, when a patient tells you that he/she will call, it never happens. Stay in control. Ask permission to call. Then make a note in your tickler file to do so!

The appointment coordinator stayed in control of this conversation and of the appointment book. When you allow the patients to control your days, their appointments, and ultimately your practice, chaos can result. Chaos breeds stress.

CREATE A WIN/WIN PRACTICE

You do your patients a tremendous service when you control your practice, because then everyone becomes a winner. Your patients win because you can give them your full attention. Your team members win, because they aren't running around in chaos and can turn their attention to patient care and maximizing their own talents. You win, because:

- you are able to provide optimum dental care more often
- you can function in a stress controlled environment
- you can take the necessary time to build and maintain excellent relationships
- you can enjoy the practice of dentistry and love what you do for a living

In Summary

Do not fear an objection, even the objection of money. Rather, look at this as an opportunity.

Know that if you do your best and the patient does not go ahead, he/she is rejecting the treatment proposal—not rejecting you.

Combine a strong belief in your team and the services you provide with the skills to communicate that message. You can learn to deal with, "Gee, Doc, it costs too much!" Let's study this "fear of cost" barrier even further.

CHAPTER 112

FINANCIAL COMMUNICATION:
THE FINAL CLOSE

"Very rarely does a business tool come along that is both good for the practice and good for the patient. Typically, there is always a trade-off but not with patient financing. I have personally witnessed practices start offering patient financing and increase their production by up to 50%. I've seen accounts receivable drop from $100,000 to virtually zero. The greatest reward, however, is when I hear from a patient that, if it weren't for patient financing, family members wouldn't have received the dentistry they needed. Now that's a win-win—that makes everyone smile!

−J. DOUGLAS HAMMOND
CARECREDIT®
VICE-PRESIDENT SALES

"Well, Doctor, I'd like to go ahead with this treatment. I know I need it. But it just costs too much! I can't afford it right now. I'll just have to wait." Have you heard this before? Does the response ever come at the completion of your excellent presentation of recommendations? Do you get discouraged? Do you wonder what you can do to deal with the objection, the barrier, and the fear of cost?

Certainly, communicating with your patients about their financial responsibility and about the options you have available for payment may be one of the most challenging conversations you will have with a patient. If you have done a beautiful presentation, and the patient wants to proceed but indicates that they are not going to do so, the reason may be the cost.

We have studied the skills of asking for a commitment during your clinical presentation. Even if the doctor or treatment coordinator gets the "go ahead" from the patient, don't be too confident. The closing on the clinical aspects of the treatment is the "pre-close." The final close comes when the patient agrees to the financial responsibility and schedules that first appointment.

Let's look at two aspects of financing:

- establishing equitable and comfortable financial options
- learning how to communicate about those options

ESTABLISHING FINANCIAL OPTIONS

For patients who need financial assistance, whether for a small case or a major multithousand-dollar case, there are ways for them to access financial assistance. However, the dentist does not have to provide the money—only the financing vehicle.

Consider this goal for your practice—make the financing of your dentistry affordable for the vast majority of your patients without doing the banking yourself. Get out of the banking business, and stay out! I often poll my audiences and ask the following questions:

- "How many of you have had professional banking training?" Most of the time, out of an audience of 100 to 1,000 people, I will get one or two hands raised
- "How many of you have had professional training in collections?" Usually, the same two hands will go up
- "How many of you are trained as loan officers?" Usually no hands go up.
- "How many of you are doing credit history checks on your patients prior to carrying their account on your own books?" Usually, five or six hands go up with this question
- "How many of you are charging some kind of a finance fee for loaning your patients money?" Usually, the same five or six hands go up

Through deductive reasoning, I then ask: "Are you saying that you are loaning your patients money without a credit history check and without a finance fee? Are you asking your wonderful team members to run a banking business even though these people have not received professional training in either banking, loaning money, or collections?" Of course, heads nod in affirmation.

Then I ask the last question of the series: "When was the last time you received an interest free loan without a credit history check?" Of course, no hands go up in response to that question.

For many years now, I have had the privilege of studying with banking and financing experts and with the people who first originated the concept of patient financing in our industry. It has been exciting to see how this concept has evolved over the years. As dentistry has evolved, so has the patient-financing concept. However, there is still only a small segment of the dental profession that is involved with patient financing, and then once a practice becomes involved, the use of the program is limited.

THE COST OF CARRYING ACCOUNTS ON YOUR OWN BOOKS

Consider doing three things:

- provide more dentistry per patient on fewer patients per day
- see the patient for fewer visits
- get out of the banking business

In terms of stress control, quality control, and profitability, doing more dentistry per patient on fewer patients per day and seeing the patient for fewer visits makes good sense. Being busy (having a patient in every chair all day long) is not necessarily the answer to increased profit. In fact, many practices are too busy.

Can you be too busy? Yes. If you are running around like chickens with your heads chopped off; if you feel you cannot give patients the time and attention needed or that you wish to give; if you cannot see patients in a timely fashion because you are too heavily booked; if you feel you do not have time to carefully plan, orchestrate, and deliver a case presentation as I have recommended; if you are so exhausted from the day's work that you have no energy left for your family when you go home, then you are too busy or the efficiency of the systems of your practice need refinement.

What do you do?

- Analyze and refine *all* of your management systems
- Give some careful study, planning, and practice to improving your case presentations, as we have discussed throughout this book
- Revamp your scheduling techniques
- Provide financing that will make it possible for people to receive quality care in a timely fashion in a stress-controlled environment

The financial options I am going to recommend will let you schedule longer appointments based on need and quality rather than on how much a patient can pay per appointment. Give patients a chance to come in and get as much done as possible so they don't have to interrupt their busy days so much and so often. Both of you will win from this type of management scenario.

Most practitioners love this model. However, many of you are not actually practicing this model, because:

- you can only do a little bit of the treatment per appointment either because your appointment book is not orchestrated properly or you don't have longer time slots available
- your patients tell you to only do a little bit because that is all they can afford or because insurance only covers so much per year

However, interview your patients and ask them the following question: "If you have decay in four areas or quadrants of your mouth, and you know that you need restorative care, and you want to get healthy and save your teeth, how would you like to schedule that treatment? Would you rather come in for four different visits? Get off work four different times for four one-hour appointments? Be anesthetized four different times? Or would you rather come in for two visits that would be approximately one and a half hours each, get off work two times, and receive anesthesia two times. Which would you prefer?"

Nine out of ten people will say, "get me in, get it done, and get me back to work." However, even though this is the scheduling they prefer, it doesn't happen often. Why? Because the amount of treatment received per visit is usually dictated by the amount the patient can afford to pay right then.

Therefore, you must:

- Work on your case presentations and scheduling so that people accept treatment
- Make sure that your appointment book doesn't work against but with you
- Offer alternative payment methods

You must be able to schedule longer appointments, and you must be able to see people expediently when they decide to proceed. Remember: The time to sell is when you have a willing buyer. If you put people off too long because you cannot fit them into your schedule, you run the risk of them not scheduling, losing the desire to proceed, or having something else come up that becomes a priority over the dental treatment.

In terms of the payment methods, be proactive about refining this system with your practice. Analyze the cost of carrying accounts on your own books (Fig. 12-1). It costs so much in time and money to carry accounts on your own books that I encourage you to stop doing that. Alternative payment methods will help both the patient and you.

In fact, if you carry an account for more than three months, the total cost to you is approximately 42.2%. Various data show that the average overhead for a general practice today ranges from 60-70%. If you are under that for your overhead, good job! However, "average practice America" loses money by carrying an account, or breaks even at best.

Fig. 12-1: *Collect What You Produce,* Pennwell Corporation

Get out of the banking business. Put the banking aspect or the credit portion of your practice into the hands of professionals—people who do have banking and collection expertise—people who *can* afford to loan money—people who *do* have the time and the focus to do just that.

Turn your time, money, and attention to doing what you do best—dentistry. Spend more time on those new patient experiences and your consultations. Spend quality time making the financial arrangement in the first place so you don't have to spend the time and money to send statements and do collections, after the fact. Spending time making the financial arrangement will save you time in the long run.

FINANCIAL OPTIONS

Consider the following financial strategies. These are the strategies that we, at Jameson Management, Inc., have integrated into more than 1,700 practices throughout the U.S. and other countries around the world. These strategies work to help more people accept your dentistry and keep you out of the banking business. Not only can your production increase significantly, but also your profit margin will do the same thing. Consider the following financial options:

- Five percent accounting reduction for payment in full before treatment begins (Do this for cases over a designated amount, to be determined by each individual practice)
- Payment by the appointment (Take the total investment, divide it by the expected number of appointments, and collect those equal amounts per appointment.)
- Bank cards
- Healthcare financing programs
    - Revolving payment plans
        - Minimum payment plans
        - Interest-free payment plans
    - Extended payment plans

(1) Accounting reduction. This gives the people who can afford to make full payment an incentive to do just that. You will be dollars ahead to get the money in the bank before treatment begins. Any time you have to wait on the money, you begin to lose. The value of the dollar decreases, the chances of the person not completing treatment increases, the possibility of a person not paying as arranged becomes an issue, and the costs of carrying accounts on your own books are prohibitive. In addition, any scheduling coordinator will tell you that if patients pay for treatment in advance, they will show up for their appointments. Therefore, do not carry accounts on your own books. You are not a bank, nor are you trained as bankers or loan officers. Stick to what you do best—dentistry.

(2) Payment by the appointment. This is done in a specific way so that the patient's financial responsibility to you is complete by the time the treatment is complete. One way is to divide the total investment by the number of appointments so that payment is completed by the conclusion of treatment. The option "payment by the appointment" is for cash, check, or bank card.

(3) Bank Cards. Do not be concerned about the service fee you will pay for the use of these financing vehicles. Again, you will be dollars ahead to get payment and not be responsible for statements or collections. The dollars you will save by not running a credit business within your practice will far outweigh any service fees you will pay.

Market bank cards to your patients as a payment option. Believe it or not, people still do not think of using their bank cards for payment of dental services. However, the bank cards are marketing heavily to consumers, encouraging them to consider this option. You can do the same thing right in your practice. Use newsletters, special mailings, and verbal skills during financial presentations to get your patients used to handling their payments with a bank card.

(4) Healthcare financing programs. For any long term or extended payments (those patients who want the treatment but need to make monthly payments and spread those payments out over several months), use a healthcare financing program. These programs have the financial wherewithal to loan your patients the monies necessary to receive treatment.

Healthcare Financing Programs

Let's talk about healthcare financing programs. As a healthcare provider, you are interested in constantly improving the services you offer. Getting involved with and promoting a healthcare financing program is one of the best services you can offer your patients and your practice. You may be asking, what are these services, and why are you describing them as a service?

A healthcare financing program is a financial vehicle that funds your patient's dental treatment. If you have accounts receivable, you are, in essence, loaning your patients money. As I indicated earlier, you may want to reconsider that. You are not a banker.

Two things happen in most dental practices:

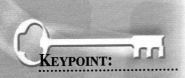

- People walk out the door not agreeing to proceed with treatment because they think they can't afford it.
- Or, they only schedule a part of the treatment based on how much they can afford and/or how much insurance will pay

So, enters the healthcare financing program. A patient comes to your practice for evaluation. You diagnose and prescribe treatment. A financial discussion takes place. If a person needs to make small monthly payments in order to afford the treatment, you offer a payment option that lets the patient spread out the payments over a period of time, keep the monthly payments small, and not have to put off that needed or desired care. Therein lies the service.

The patients win. More people are able to receive quality dental care without compromise. The practice wins. Cash flow increases because of a higher level of treatment acceptance. Overhead is reduced, thus increasing the profit margin of the practice. Why? The costs paid by the practice to the financing company are significantly lower than the costs of running a banking business within your practice. "A penny saved is a penny earned." In addition, the people running these healthcare-financing programs are professional financial experts. It is a wiser and better use of time for the dentist and team to focus on dentistry, practice building, and customer service—being people professionals.

How do these programs work?

The patient fills out an application in your practice and does not have to go anywhere else. Once the patient has been given a line of credit, you do the dentistry, get paid, and the patient begins receiving statements from your financial partner.

There are numerous types of programs on the market today. The different types of programs have been developed as a result of demands from the industry, both on the part of patients and practices.

1. Revolving payment plans. A line of credit is established for the family. This line of credit can be used, serviced, and used again (just like a bank card.) You will see more people going ahead with full treatment rather than doing one crown a year. You will see more members of the family proceeding with treatment and staying steadily involved with the hygiene department. And, so on.

These revolving payment plans are of two types:

- *Minimum payment due*—Spread out as long as is necessary. A percentage of the outstanding balance is the minimum payment. (For example, 3%)
- *3, 6, or 12-month interest free*—The patient must charge a specific amount with these programs and must be able to conclude payments by the pre-determined time allotment. However, they can extend their payment timeframe, if necessary, and will then fall into the category above. A minimum payment (usually 3% of the balance) is due monthly.

2. Extended payment. Twenty-four-to-sixty-month financing with specifically determined payments (much like a car loan). Low interest rates. Low service fees to the doctor. These are great programs for the larger cases—implants, full mouth reconstruction, and cosmetic cases. There is a low limit ($1,000) and a high maximum ($25,000+).

Get involved with these programs. Learn how to present these options. The verbal skills/presentation skills are critical for the success of the program. Learn how to address the very common objections that patients will present. Learn how to promote the program. Both you and the patients will benefit.

OVERCOMING OBJECTIONS
TO FINANCING PROGRAMS

Below are common patient concerns and the verbal skills that will help you:

- get patients involved with your healthcare financing program
- gain patient cooperation if you are changing your financial protocol

Patient: "I've been paying Dr. Smith forever. Why can't I just keep on paying him the way I always have?"

Financial Coordinator: "I can understand your confusion about this change. However, we have changed accounting methods and are no longer able to carry long-term accounts on our own books. We found that it wasn't time or cost effective for us to carry accounts. Now we have become associated with a super company, [Name of Company], that works with us to offer convenient financing for our patients. We're committed to maintaining reasonable fees for our services. So, we searched for a better, more cost-efficient way to offer long-term financing to patients. [Company name] has become an important part of our dental team. We have always been committed to comfortable dentistry, and now we are able to extend that comfort into the area of financing as well."

Patient: "Tell me more about this company. I don't understand this."

Financial Coordinator: "[Company Name] is a financing company for dentistry. By having such a program for your health care, you can conveniently budget this vital service into your monthly income."

Patient: "I don't know about this. Is this a difficult thing to do?"

Financial Coordinator: "Not at all. The application is very easy. In fact, you apply right here in our office. The application will be similar to any application you have filled out previously, but if you do have any questions, I'd be glad to help you. We can send your application right over the Internet and will know immediately if the company is able to extend a line of credit to you. Then we will be able to go ahead and schedule your first appointment. I know you are anxious to begin treatment. That beautiful smile can be yours."

Patient: "Will they charge me interest?"

(NOTE: I will give two different verbal scenarios due to the interest-free programs and the revolving-payment plans.)

KEYPOINT:

An objection
is an opportunity.

Interest-free program

Financial Coordinator: "Believe it or not, Mr. Patient, there will be no interest charged. You will need to make a minimum payment per month, which is 3% of the outstanding balance. But, if you pay off the entire amount by the time frame you select, there will be no interest charged at all. If for any reason you cannot pay this off in the selected time frame, you have a safety net. Your account will convert to a revolving payment plan where you can continue to make a minimum payment per month. However, I do want you to know that if you cannot pay the full amount in the designated time frame, you will be charged all back interest. So, it is important that we work together to find a time frame that suits you. However, I want you to know that if you find that things get tight for you, you will still have that safety net to fall back on."

Revolving-payment plan

Financial Coordinator: "Yes. Just like other financing programs, a service fee is involved. This fee is 1.75% or approximately $1.75 per month for every hundred dollars that you finance. That's not much considering the fact that you can now have those veneers that you have wanted for so long and the monthly investment will fit your situation." (Use the figures and percentages appropriate to your program.)

Patient: "I don't know about this! I just wish I could pay Dr. Smith the way I used to!"

Financial Coordinator: "I know how you feel. We have had other good, long-term patients who have felt the same way until they found they could still pay out their dentistry. In fact, their monthly payments are usually smaller, and they can take longer to pay their account. We have many families utilizing the [Company Name] plan. They love the convenience. These families seem happier not owing the doctor, and because of their available credit line, they can take better care of more members of their families."

Handling the cost objection

Remember: an objection, including the objection of cost, is actually a step forward in completing an agreement.

If you know that cost is going to be brought up as an objection, you bring it up first. This gives you an opportunity to turn a potential negative into a positive.

For example:

Doctor: "Mr. Patient, before I give you the results of my analysis, and before I explain the treatment that I am going to recommend for you, first let me tell you that if you have any concerns about the financing of your treatment, we do have convenient, long-term financing right here in our practice. I tell you this, so that for now, we can both concentrate on the treatment I am recommending. We will discuss financial options in full. We want to make sure that you are clear and comfortable with this important part of your treatment. But for now, I would like us to focus on the treatment I am recommending, the treatment that I believe would help you reach your goals. Is that okay with you?"

After you have made your presentation of recommendations and have answered all questions about the treatment, if the patient expresses a concern about the money, then ask this question:

Doctor: "Is the financing of the dentistry a concern for you?"

Patient: "Yes. I'm sure this will cost quite a bit."

Doctor: "I can appreciate your concern. That's why Jan is joining us today. She will discuss the total fee and the options we have available for payment. We have some great options, and I'm sure she will be able to work this out with you. Once we work out the financial arrangement, is there any other reason why we shouldn't go ahead?"

Patient: "No, I want to do this. I just need a way to pay for it."

Or:

Doctor: "Mr. Patient, if I understand you correctly, this is the type of dentistry you would like to receive, is this right?"

Patient: "Yes."

Doctor: "Then, if we are able to make the financing of the dentistry comfortable for you, is there any reason why we shouldn't go ahead and schedule an appointment to begin your treatment?"

Other Common Financial Objections

Objection #1

Patient: "That costs too much."

Business Administrator: "You feel the fee is too high for the services we are recommending for you? Or is the investment difficult for you at this time?"

Patient: "I'm sure the treatment is worth the fee, but I can't afford this right now. That just costs too much!"

Business Administrator: "I know how you feel, Mr. Patient, today most things do. Tell me, Mr. Patient, if we can make the financing comfortable for you with a convenient monthly payment, would this make it possible for you to proceed?"

Patient: "Probably."

Business Administrator: "How much per month could you invest?"

His answer to this question would let you know if you could go ahead by offering him MasterCard, Visa, Discover, or a healthcare financing program.

Objection #2

Patient: "Well, I want those veneers. I hate my smile. But $3,000 is just too much!"

Treatment Coordinator: "How much too much is that, Mr. Patient?"

Patient: "About $1,500 too much. I saved $1,500 for this, but wow, I had no idea it would be this much!"

Treatment Coordinator: "So, the solution we're looking for is a way to finance the $1,500 beyond your savings program, is that right?"

Patient: "Yes."

Now you know that the $3,000 isn't the problem. It's the $1,500 of the treatment that needs attention and assistance.

Objection #3

Patient: "I'll have to think about this!"

Financial Coordinator: "Thank you, Mr. Patient. I'm sure that you wouldn't take the time to think about the treatment if you weren't interested. In order for me to be clear as to what you need to think about, let me ask you, is it the treatment itself you need to think about, or is this the type of dental care you'd like to receive?"

Patient: "I want the treatment. I know this is what I need! I'm sick of the mess in my mouth."

Financial Coordinator: "Then, are you unsure about us providing your treatment?"

Patient: "Oh, no. I wouldn't have come here if I didn't trust you guys!"

Financial Coordinator: "Well, may I ask, is it the investment? Are you concerned about the money?"

Patient: "Yes! I had no idea it would cost this much to get my teeth fixed! I don't know if I can afford this right now."

Financial Coordinator: "If we are able to make the financing of the dentistry comfortable for you, would that make it possible for you to go ahead with the recommended treatment?"

Patient: "Well, yes. If I can pay it out."

Financial Coordinator: "OK. If we are able to arrange convenient financing, is there any other reason why we should not proceed with your treatment?"

Patient: "No, not really."

Financial Coordinator: "Mr. Patient, I'm going to spend some time with you discussing our financial options. We have some wonderful options, and I feel very confident that we will be able to work this out with you. The last thing we want is for the fee to get in the way of you receiving the treatment you need."

This is a closing sequence in which the financial coordinator responded to the patient's questions or statements with another question or with a clarifying response. He or she didn't jump to any conclusions; didn't offer solutions, make judgments, or give advice; and did not become offended or angered by the patient's concern about the fee.

This closing sequence does the following:

- Gives the patient a chance to uncover the barriers
- Lets the financial coordinator clarify how many and what kinds of obstacles are present
- Asks a closing question that leads a patient to make a decision

The problem is not totally solved! The financial coordinator has "preclosed." He/she has determined that the patient does want the treatment. However, there is a barrier or problem. Now that the problem has been uncovered, there can be a solution found. The financial coordinator would move into the seven processes of problem-solving (see Chapter 7).

Objection #4

Patient: "If my insurance doesn't cover this, I can't get it done."

Business Administrator: "Mrs. Patient, it is great that you have dental insurance. Our patients have found that dental insurance is a wonderful supplement to their healthcare. However, insurance is not a "pay all." It is a supplement. Dr. Jameson has recommended treatment that is necessary for the restoration of your mouth. We will do everything to help you maximize your insurance benefits. Based on information and experience with your insurance company, we can estimate very closely what we expect them to pay. You will be responsible for the balance. However, we want you to know that we have excellent payment options available in our practice and can assist you with that balance.

Mrs. Patient, how much per month would you be willing and able to invest?"

Financing the Aesthetic Case

One of the most fulfilling aspects of being a dental professional is being able to make a positive change in a person's smile, a change that will enhance a person's self worth and self confidence. The rewards of providing cosmetic dental care are many:

- The challenge of performing highly intricate dental procedures
- Enhancing a person's self image
- Using one's artistic and clinical skills to the maximum degree
- Having patients want to be in the chair
- Receiving expressions of gratitude instead of complaints
- Healthy financial reward for your expertise

However, with few exceptions, cosmetic dental treatment will require a significant investment. If the financing of the dentistry is a concern or barrier to a person being able to proceed, what are your options?

- Don't do the dentistry
- Only do one tooth at a time (which in many cases is less than aesthetic!)
- Carry the account on your own books, letting patients make small monthly payments directly to you

- Do the dentistry for free
- Do aesthetic/cosmetic dentistry only on the wealthy population
- Design payment options that will make the financing of the aesthetic case comfortable for the majority of your patients while keeping you out of the banking business

Of course, the last option is the option of choice. Offering convenient payment options (such as the ones just discussed) to your patients addresses one of the major reasons why people do not proceed with treatment—the cost. If you can overcome this objection, more people will agree to aesthetic/cosmetic dental treatment. Insurance obviously is not a supplement for aesthetic care. Therefore, the financial options discussed will clear the way for many patients.

Many people do not give themselves permission to invest in this type of dentistry, because they don't think it's okay to spend money on treatment that improves appearance. Even though you and I know that this type of treatment not only improves appearance but also improves self-image and self-esteem, there are many people who just can't give themselves permission to spend money on themselves. If you present your case as aesthetically as you will do the dentistry, people will get excited about what's available in dentistry today. Then, if you handle the financing in such a manner that the investment doesn't have a negative effect on their financial situation, you may be able to help them get to the point where they can psychologically feel good about the investment.

Benefits

There are numerous benefits to the financial options that I have recommended. Benefits to patients:

- small monthly payments
- longer time-frame in which to pay their balance
- not having to postpone or reject treatment
- owing you nothing

Benefits to the practice:

- improved cash flow

- carrying no accounts on your own books
- reduced costs, since you are not running a banking business in your practice
- increased productivity, because more people will proceed with treatment
- clearer understanding of financial responsibility by the patients, thus, fewer disgruntled patients
- team members do not have to spend time or money on statements and collections
- reduced broken appointments and no shows

In Summary

By carefully developing an excellent financial system in your practice and by learning how to present the options, overcome objections, and defuse the fear of cost, you take the lid off your practice productivity. By offering the recommended options, dentists win because they get to do the kind of dentistry they have been so carefully taught to do. Their production goes up significantly when they proactively promote convenient financing.

Patients win because they don't have to put off needed or desired care if they can't come up with large amounts of money at one time. That's what I call WIN-WIN.

The financial communication you have with a patient is a very intimate kind of conversation. The oral cavity is an intimate part of a person's body and so is the pocketbook! How you handle this very personal communication will go a long way toward building strong relationships with your patients and increasing the production of your practice.

CHAPTER

13

NURTURE PERSONAL REFERRALS — YOUR BEST SOURCE OF NEW PATIENTS

Many people refuse to delegate to other people because they feel it takes too much time and effort and they could do the job better themselves. But effectively delegating to others is perhaps the single most powerful high leverage activity there is.

— STEPHEN R. COVEY

Without question, your number one source of new patients has been, and always will be, personal referrals. In fact, if you are in general practice, approximately 70% of your new patients will come to you as a result of personal referrals. If this is the case, then everyone on the team must be given and must receive the responsibility and commission to nurture those referrals. By doing so, you will be delegating the responsibility for building your practice to all members of the team and to the hundreds of patients who are already a part of your organization. As Dr. Covey says, delegation may be the "single, most powerful leverage activity there is."

Throughout this book, we have studied how to communicate effectively so your patients will recognize your professionalism and your commitment to quality. We have learned how to deal with difficult people and difficult situations so you can turn those challenging situations into great relationships. We have studied the intricate skills of case presentation and handling objections, so more people will accept the treatment that you are recommending, and communicating financially.

Now, let's continue the flow of communication by turning happy patients into referral sources—people who willingly recommend you to their friends and family members.

IDENTIFY AND NURTURE REFERRAL SOURCES

Ask for referrals

Everyone on the team must become comfortable with asking for referrals. When a patient expresses gratitude, has completed treatment, has received a beautiful new smile, etc., ask that person for referrals.

For example:

Mrs. Jones: *"I just love my new smile. I feel SO great!"*

Doctor or team member: "Thank you, Mrs. Jones. We appreciate your kind words. Mrs. Jones, we build our practice on excellent patients like you and we love creating those beautiful smiles. Do you have friends or family members who need a dental home?"

Mrs. Jones: *"Oh, yes, lots of them."*

Doctor or team member: "May we give you a few of our cards (or office brochures) and ask you to tell your friends and family members about our practice? When they come to us, we will take excellent care of them, just as we have tried to do with you."

People will be happy to refer their friends to you. Ask! Believe in what you're doing, and ask your solid clients or patients to give their support to you. Let your patient family become your sales force. Leverage!

Acknowledge referral sources with a "thank you for referral" note

Business experts tell us that one of the most effective ways to solidify or expand a relationship with a client is to write notes. As simple as this may seem, it works. Acknowledging and expressing your gratitude goes a long way.

Either produce your own "thank you for referral" notes or purchase notes from a supplier. Keep these notes in the business office with a specific person assigned the responsibility for completing and tracking these notes.

The task becomes manageable if you sign and address these cards every day. Leave them to do all at once, and all of a sudden it becomes an overwhelming task, one that is sometimes left undone! Keep this effort simple! If the task doesn't become overwhelming, it will be done on a regular, consistent basis (Fig. 13-1).

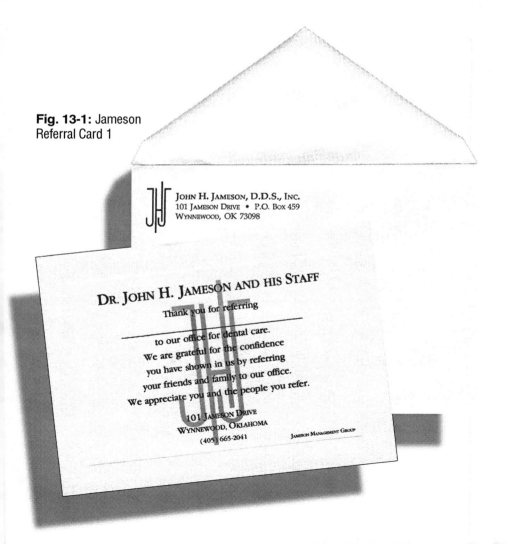

Fig. 13-1: Jameson Referral Card 1

John H. Jameson, D.D.S., Inc.
101 Jameson Drive • P.O. Box 459
Wynnewood, OK 73098

Dr. John H. Jameson and his Staff

Thank you for referring

_____

to our office for dental care.
We are grateful for the confidence
you have shown in us by referring
your friends and family to our office.
We appreciate you and the people you refer.

101 Jameson Drive
Wynnewood, Oklahoma
(405) 665-2041

Jameson Management Group

Give gifts as an expression of thanks to your referral sources

Consider providing an added value benefit to your new patients, and involve the referrer. Added value marketing is a proven incentive to a new client.

Produce a gift certificate that you can place in the hands of your regular patients. The patient of record will be the giver of the gift. Ask your patients to give this gift certificate to their friends and family members. You can make the gift whatever you wish. Some offices give a complimentary evaluation or consultation.

Track the number of referrals a person provides. When a certain goal is reached (determined by you), give your referring patient a reward for their support: i.e. a percentage fee reduction on their next procedure or appointment (Fig. 13.2).

In other words—incent both the new patient that comes to you and incent your patients to refer.

Care Enough to Share...

This entitles bearer to a complimentary consultation.

Recommended by _____

Date _____

Fig. 13-2: Referral Card 2

COMPLIMENTARY ORAL HEALTH SUPPLIES

In our own office, we distribute certificates called "A Gift of Health." Everyone on the team gives these cards to existing patients and asks satisfied clients to refer their friends and family members to the practice.

The gift certificate is for a 6-month supply of toothbrushes (12) to be received upon completion of a comprehensive oral evaluation. On the certificate is a brief synopsis of the studies by Dr. Richard Glass, formerly of the University of Oklahoma College of Dentistry, about the need to change toothbrushes every two weeks. With this certificate and the corresponding gift, we are providing added-value marketing, and we are educating people about excellent health.

When a person refers a certain number of people or when a certain amount of dentistry is provided as a result of those referrals, we give the referral source a complimentary oral hygiene device, such as an oral irrigation system or an electric toothbrush (Figs. 13-3 and 13-4).

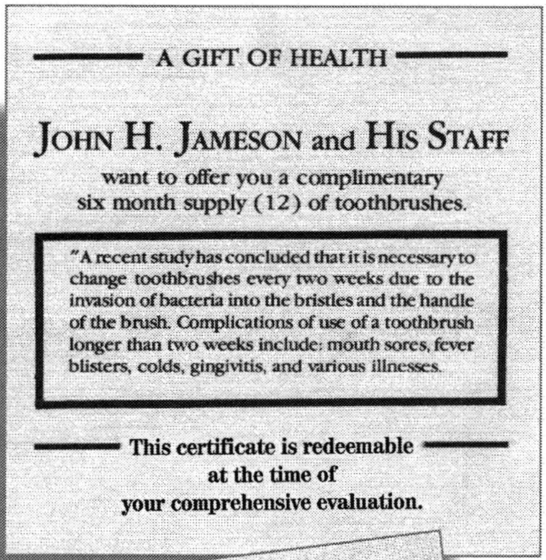

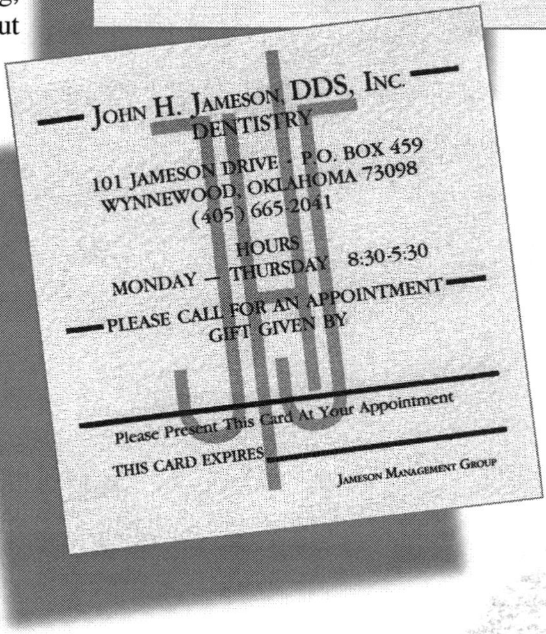

Fig. 13-3: Gift of Health Card—
an example of added-value marketing (front view; top).

Fig. 13-4: Gift of Health Card (back view; bottom).

Coffee mugs

When a patient refers another person to your practice, send him/her a coffee mug either with "thank you" balloons attached or filled with a flower arrangement, coffee, etc. Have the mugs imprinted with your logo on one side and your name, address, and phone number on the other. Keep these at a local floral shop. Call the shop to place the order. Then send this "thank you" to the referring person's place of employment.

You will hope that the referrer will carry that mug around the office, happily sipping on coffee and simultaneously placing your name in front of lots of people. Another marketing principle is at work here—you need to let people know who you are, where you are, and what you do. In addition, people need to see your name over and over and over. Repetition is an essential ingredient of good marketing.

Send complimentary theater tickets or gift certificates for dinner

Many theaters and restaurants will give you special rates if you make an arrangement to refer on a regular basis. Schedule a time to discuss the possibilities with the owner or manager of the facility.

When a person earns this wonderful gift, send a special note on your letterhead stationery that includes the gift certificate. Keep track of what you are sending and how much you are sending. It may benefit you to send these reports to the managers from time to time so they are aware of the health of your business to them. Then they may become a referral source for you. In fact, you may begin to see patients coming to you that are employed in the restaurant or theater.

Fee reduction

If a person continues to refer people who become actively involved with treatment, you may choose to thank that person by giving a fee reduction. You may give a gift discount at their next appointment for having sent you a significant amount of new business.

Again, following the lead of excellent business leaders, know where your business is coming from and nurture that source. When you scratch their backs, they will scratch yours. People love the recognition, and everyone loves a fee break. Track your referral sources and the amount of dentistry that is produced as a result of their referrals.

Network with other professionals

Identify businesses in your area that attract people with similar backgrounds to your patient family (e.g., physicians, pharmacists, bankers, optometrists, etc.). Schedule an appointment with the leader of the organization, and discuss the services you offer. Ask if you may leave brochures about your services with them, and ask that they refer people to you who might need your services.

Spend some quality listening time discovering new information about the services that they are offering. Enthusiastically and sincerely let them know that you will refer people to them who might need their services. Then do so. Make sure that when you send one of your patients to another professional or business that you send a card with the patient. Ask that they give the card to the particular professional so they will know that you have referred them.

Stay in close contact with these other professionals. Visit with them on a regular basis. Let them know that you want a solid, long-term relationship with them. Make personal visits to their practices or places of business and invite them to come to your facility. These contacts do not have to be made by the doctor. Other members of the team who are interested in and comfortable with public relations and marketing can be excellent ambassadors for the practice.

Many of the specialists that are clients of Jameson Management, Inc. have special lunches for their referring practices. The members of the teams like to get acquainted just as much as the doctors. In addition, these lunches will give you a chance to tell the referring practices what you are doing and how your services might benefit their clients.

Be ever aware of the fact that the members of the team can be as influential in referring a patient as the doctor. They also will have solid relationships with the patients. The patients will listen to and value their opinion and statements of referral and confidence.

In addition, specialists will often sponsor an educational seminar for their referring doctors and their teams. This complimentary seminar, which usually includes lunch, will be a powerful way to say thanks and to continue the referrals.

Stay in front of those referral sources. That is one of the most critical factors underlying a successful referral system.

Interact with other appearance specialists

Place information about the services of other appearance specialists in your office. Network with these people. Once a person has completed a certain type of treatment, such as full mouth reconstruction or cosmetic dentistry, send them to a salon for a makeover, or to a photography studio for a sitting, or give them a one-month membership to a health spa, etc. The money that you will invest will serve as a "thank you" to the patient, but it will also stimulate referrals from the appearance company.

Be sure that they know you are referring. Personally make the contact and the arrangements for your patient, so that the appearance specialist will know you are the referral source. Then ask if you may place your information in their facility and in their hands. They will be happy to reciprocate.

Give complimentary oral health supplies for sending a certain number of referrals

When a person refers a certain number of people or when a certain amount of dentistry is provided as a result of those referrals, give that referral source a complimentary oral hygiene device, such as an oral irrigation system or an electric tooth-brushing device.

Frequent referrer program

The world knows about and loves "frequent anything" programs! I have frequent flyer cards for every airline, frequent parking at several airports, frequent resident programs at all the hotel chains, frequent purchaser cards for bookstores, clothing stores, hosiery departments, etc. You name it! There are "frequent programs" for everything.

In John's practice and in our management firm, we pay for most of our payables with a frequent flyer credit card and then make sure that it is paid in full before any interest is charged. It is an easy step and thousands of miles are accumulated. You probably do the same thing.

Since the world is so used to and motivated by these programs, why not start your own? Have cards made up much like your business cards. You could put numbers across the bottom and use a hole punch to identify each time a person refers. You could punch the card when they come in. Check your referral list on your computer and make punches if referrals have been made. Or, you could keep track of this in your computer and send the patient a note about the referrals as they occur. When they have achieved a pre-determined bonus, send them the notice. Make it fun. Make it exciting. This is a tremendous way to build your practice with very little investment.

Determine the bonus program. What are you going to give for each level of referral? For example:

One referral—coffee mug

Two referrals—12 toothbrushes

Three referrals—complimentary dental cleaning and evaluation

Four referrals—dinner for two @_____

Five referrals—10 % off their next dental appointment

The above are just some thoughts on how to organize the bonus program. You know how bonus programs work. You accumulate so many points, and the more you accumulate, the better the gift. I would give gifts all along and increase the value of the gifts as the number of referrals increases. Be creative. Consider designing your own program with incentives that work for you

FIVE IMPORTANT STEPS
FOR NURTURING REFERRALS

1. Send every new patient a "thank you" for choosing your practice. Include two business cards
2. When a patient refers someone to your practice, send him/her a thank you. Include two business cards
3. Handle any problem quickly and succinctly. An immediately remedied problem can lead a person to being an ambassador for your practice
4. Fulfill every promise you make. People must be able to count on you to do what you say, and that means everyone on the team
5. Stay in touch with your patient family on a regular basis in a positive and constructive way

IN SUMMARY

Design a plan that will work and then work the plan. In your morning meetings, identify those patients who would be ideal candidates for referrals (patients who have expressed pleasure in receiving treatment from you). Determine who is going to ask for that referral. You wouldn't want to have everyone ask for a referral, so designate that responsibility.

Be sure that you have done some role-playing and have practiced the verbal skills of asking for a referral. Get comfortable asking. Know that you will never know what you will get unless you ask! All good businesses ask for referrals from their best customers. Learn from the masters. Pattern your own behavior after those who have acquired admirable results.

When you identify patients who have accepted and been pleased with your treatment—patients who have come to their appointments on time; patients who have paid their bills and been glad to do so; and patients who have been a joy to treat, ask these folks for a referral. More than likely, they will refer others to you who are of like character.

Together, as a team, develop ways of acknowledging and nurturing your referral sources. If these wonderful people provide 70+% of your new patients, it benefits you to invest time and money in maximizing this source of practice growth.

CONTROLLING STRESS IN THE DENTAL PROFESSION THROUGH EFFECTIVE COMMUNICATION: A DOCTORAL DISSERTATION

*"You can become productive
without being self destructive."*

— ROBERT ELIOT, M.D.

*O*ne of the hypotheses I tested during my doctoral study was that when a team of dental professionals participated in a course on communication skills training, stress would be controlled. Indeed, I was able to prove through validating research that this hypothesis was true. As you learn to improve your communication skills and apply those improved skills to your life, stress will be controlled.

In this chapter of *Great Communication = Great Production*, I will share a small bit of the research on stress management that was a part of my doctoral work. Throughout the entire book, pieces of the doctoral study have been interspersed. I have made an effort to make this book a teaching tool as much as an academic work. So, in this chapter, I will continue that pattern. I will give you information on the entire issue of stress—the impact of controlled versus uncontrolled stress, the factors that might lead to stress, ways to handle stress in addition to the communication skills, and some proven stress management strategies. My goal is for this chapter to be a guideline. Take the information in this chapter and integrate it into your life. Control your stress so it doesn't control you. Let stress be a positive rather than a destructive force in your life. The choice is yours.

IDENTIFYING THE PROBLEM

Do you remember step one of problem-solving—identifying or defining the problem? That's also the first step to stress control—identifying your own stressors. My theory is that communicative skill will not only impact your productivity, but it will also impact your stress level. In addition, in my opinion, the three issues cannot be separated—communicative skills, productivity, and stress control.

The dental environment can be extremely stressful, and that can take away from your ability or willingness to communicate. If you are overwhelmed with stress in your life, it may be easier to ignore or avoid difficult people and difficult situations. If stress becomes a dominant force in your life, you may be so short tempered that you don't have the available patience to communicate when you or the other people in your life need it.

WHAT IS STRESS?

Do you have any stress on the job? If you answered "yes," then welcome to the modern day workplace! Stress is a fact of life in business and in dentistry today. A certain amount of stress is good! It can be motivational. Without a certain amount of stress, success and achievement would be diminished. However, too much stress or uncontrolled stress can be detrimental to the health and well being of individual members of your organization and to the overall health and productivity of the organization itself. Stress that becomes debilitating is termed distress.

According to Dr. Carl Caplan in *Dental Practice Management Encyclopedia*, the term stress refers to "the physiological and psychological responses of an individual to demands from the environment (termed stressors)." William H. Hendrix, Ph.D. defines *stress* as "an individual's cognitive interpretation (or appraisal) of internal or external events judged (consciously or unconsciously) to be threatening, harmful or challenging."

This definition indicates that different stressors affect different people in different ways. A situation that might be perceived as stressful to one person on your team might not be at all stressful to another.

Peter Hanson, M.D., in his book *Stress for Success*, states, "Stress is 80% of all illnesses. On the other hand, stress is also the key to excellence. Stress does not actually cause excellence, nor does it actually cause illness or financial losses. In fact, stress is neutral until it lands on a person. What that person has chosen to do about past stresses, and what the person chooses to do in response to present stress, will determine the outcome."

Dr. Hanson points out "the answers to the problems of stress control are within the grasp of each individual. Each of us, as a manager of his or her own Department of One, has the power to break out of the lemming herd and turn away from the precipice that awaits the incompetent stress handler."

Uncontrolled stress can affect the mind. It can take its toll on emotional well-being while it drains energy and vitality from you. This can lead to irritability and quick temper. Stress can distort the way you think and feel about yourself. Unbridled, stress can chip away at your own feeling of self-worth—your self-esteem. Stress can affect your relationship with others, making it difficult to relate in a constructive way with people at work and outside of work. Stress can also drain the energy you need to participate in your community activities.

C. Maslach in his article, "Burn Out," (*Human Behavior*, 1976) states that health and social service professionals are particularly vulnerable to mental and physical strain and exhaustion because of the work they do, which is "caring for deeply troubled people, day after day." In their article, "Conspicuous in its Absence: The Lack of Positive

KEYPOINT:

Too much stress or uncontrolled stress can be detrimental to the health and well being of individual members of your organization and to the overall health and productivity of the organization itself. Stress that becomes debilitating is termed distress.

KEYPOINT:

Unbridled, stress can chip away at your own feeling of self-worth— your self-esteem.

Conditions as a Source of Stress" (*Journal of Human Stress*, 1978), Kanner, Kafry, and Pines note that the reactions to work-related stress often take the form of acute attitudinal, emotional, and physical exhaustion, which they termed "tedium." This concept is similar to the principle of "burnout," which is defined as a "wearing out" from heavy demands. M. Daley, in his article, "Burnout: Smoldering Problem in Protective Services" (*Socialwork*, 1979), provides the following description: "Burnout is a dynamic process with identifiable phases of development. These developmental phases are manifested so slowly that the healthcare worker may be oblivious to the symptoms or deny there is any problem. Yet, when staff experience exhaustion from the rigors of patient and practice interaction, the individual, the organization and the patients may suffer for a long time."

Dr. William Hendrix states in his article, "Dental Stress and Assessment Questionnaire," (*Dental Clinics of North America*, 1986), three main factors lead to perceived stress among professionals in the workplace today. They are:

- job related factors
- external or non-job related factors
- individual or personal characteristics

How do these three main factors affect the practice? Let's look at each of these.

Job related factors

The organizational climate of a dental practice is substantially related to stress. The better the organization of the practice, the more controlled the stress levels for all team members. Poor organization, or total lack of organization, is a major source of stress for all involved.

Organization and management can be divided into three specific areas:

- Business management
- Personnel management
- Patient management

Specific organizational or management deficiencies that lead to stress within these three areas are as follows:

Business management

- Lack of procedures, policies, or processes for dealing with the business systems of the practice, i.e., scheduling, financial arrangements, insurance management, time management, etc.
- Equipment problems or insufficiently equipped treatment rooms
- The working environment itself—the facility
- Cash flow—profitability or lack thereof

Personnel management

- Interpersonal conflict
- Poor leadership
- Burnout
- Staff turnover
- Ineffective communication

Patient management

- Managing difficult or fearful patients
- Dealing with non-acceptance of treatment recommendations
- Patients who refuse to maintain oral health following treatment
- Patients who cancel appointments with little or no notice
- Patients who refuse to pay their bills

In addition to these organizational and management issues, the physical aspects of performing the dentistry also ignite the stress response. The performance of dentistry is extremely tedious. All five senses are constantly stimulated. There is a perceived concept that there is no margin for error, thus imbedding the perfectionist syndrome.

The environment in which the clinical team works is extremely small. The body position that must be assumed is physically taxing, and held over a period of time, adds stress and strain to nerve and muscle alike. Additional environmental factors that might add to stress include room temperatures, loud noises, air pollution, malfunctioning equipment, inadequate lighting, and poor equipment design. Inefficient work methods due to poor equipment design subject dental professionals to considerable fatigue, which in turn, makes them more susceptible to psychological stress.

Many dentists and dental auxiliaries feel that everyone must like them, and they must like everyone. In the event that the dental professionals experience lack of acceptance or even outright rejection by some people, they might (and often do) feel they are not okay. This rejection indicates (to them) imperfection. Being confronted with the reality of interpersonal relationships, and their own limitations, becomes stressful.

In their study of "Dental Family Stress and Coping Patterns" (*Dental Clinics of North America*, 1986), Nevin and Sampson state "inability to accept limitations is a problem common to many people in dentistry and a great source of stress for many dentists in particular." In fact, Nevin and Sampson found that 64% of the dentists they surveyed said that perfectionism was their greatest source of stress.

The entire team is often negatively affected when a patient experiences discomfort. The team's entire purpose is to eliminate discomfort and gain and ensure health. For patients to fear them as pain inflictors, however misperceived, is often debilitating to dental professionals.

External or non-job related factors

- Family relationships
- Commuting time and distance
- Economic factors
- Demands placed on an individual by the community
- Social activities

Family relationships are often the most significant external factors leading to excessive stress. Sometimes families receive the stress inflicted by the dental professional, or sometimes it is the family itself that is the producer of stress for the dentist or the dental auxiliary. Stress in dentistry can have a strong and direct effect on the physical well being of both the dentist and the spouse. When the dentist is feeling upset or stressed out, the spouse is likely to be the same.

The stressors that seem to emerge as the most intense for dental families are finance and business strains (changes in the financial conditions of the practice, affecting available funds for family use).

Dental families experience stress that arises from both the dental practice and family-related issues. Stable dental families exercise effort to maintain a sense of balance through effective coping skills and family resources. The results of Nevin and Sampson's study of dental family stress and coping patterns indicated that "strong coping patterns resulted when dental professionals and spouses maintained a balance of time and responsibility, satisfaction in work and family activity, regular communication, sharing of decision-making, good physical health and the inclusion of an active exercise program within multiple demands of their time."

Individual and personality characteristics

Personality characteristics play a significant part in how an individual deals with stressors. As was previously indicated, certain stressors generate different actions and reactions from different people. One of the main reasons behind this is that different people wear different character make-ups.

Most generally, behavior types fall under two distinct categories—Type A behavior is characterized by excessive aggressiveness, time urgency, restlessness, hostility, and tenseness. Type A dental professionals have been found to be behind schedule more frequently then Type B dental professionals.

Type B characteristics are flexibility, ability to relax, control, and acceptance. Type B individuals feel in control of their lives in comparison to Type A personalities, who feel others control their lives and that external forces have a stronger effect on them than internal forces.

EFFECTS OF STRESS

Stress affects people both physiologically and psychologically. Psychologically, stress "takes the form of a subjective sense of discomfort and distress, distortions in thinking, decreased performance and indecisiveness." These psychological effects may lead to:

- lack of desire to go to work
- absenteeism
- tardiness
- poor or altered performance

- difficulty in getting along with peers/co-workers
- turnover

Physiologically, the stress response consists of a coordinated set of bodily responses signaled by a release of hormones and sympathetic nervous system stimulation.

Physiological effects of stress may lead to:

- high blood pressure and other coronary problems
- ulcers and other digestive problems
- illness such as colds and flu
- headaches and migraines
- sleeping disorders
- lowered efficiency of the immune system

Physiological and psychological consequences of stress, although separate, are nevertheless interrelated. Illnesses resulting from stress will definitely have an effect on job performance, presence on the job, attitude on the job, etc. Conversely, poor attitude about work, conflicting interpersonal relationships among co-workers, and outside negative influences, such as financial difficulties and marital problems, can lead to high blood pressure and the other above-mentioned physiological diseases.

Stress, when left unbridled, can become detrimental to one's mental and physical health. A common thread runs through the lives of most people who fall prey to the potentially devastating effects of uncontrolled stress. This thread is that most of the stress could have been tamed or controlled. Total mismanagement of stress has led to illnesses, misery, and even death.

The correctable nature of much of this mismanaged illness is not to say that the results are not debilitating. Not in the least. The devastating effects are concrete, no doubt about it:

- Physically—people get sick. They often die earlier
- Financially—people do not perform at their best
- Emotionally—people are not at their peak and do not handle their relationships or themselves well
- Spiritually—people are often depressed and lay blame. They choose not to develop a close spiritual relationship

In spite of books, tapes, and courses on the subject of stress control or stress management and personal development, many people do not choose to manage themselves healthily. This is reflected in illness and death statistics, in the quality of people's daily lives, and ultimately, in the enormous loss of profits in business which amount to tens of billions of dollars per year.

SIGNS OF POOR SELF MANAGEMENT

- Low energy
- Decreased productivity
- Lowered self image/self esteem
- Poor decision making
- More mistakes
- Accidents
- Illness
- Tardiness and/or absenteeism
- Burnout
- Problems with personal relationships at home and at work
- Poor financial management
- Shortened longevity

Those people who choose not to take personal responsibility for the control of stress in their lives, but blame their job, other people, or circumstances for their problems, are selecting a self-destructive route. When days get full and hectic, the thing that usually falls by the wayside is time spent for personal management—exercise, eating properly, relaxation, time with kids, spouse, or self, etc.

You are responsible to yourself. You are the manager of yourself. If you think you are special, you are! However, you are not so special that you are immune to the risks of poor personal management. Workaholics, alcoholics, drug abusers, cigarette smokers, and obese people think that problems are going to happen to someone else. Wrong! You must run your body/mind with the same expertise that you run your practice.

Again, stress cannot be eliminated, nor would you want to eliminate it. The challenge is to learn how to control or manage your personal response to stress. Those who choose to actively and constructively control their stress can learn to harness stress and turn this potentially harmful force into high-powered energy.

"The same stress which makes one person sick can be an invigorating experience for another," according to Dr. Hans Selye. "It is though the General Adaptation Syndrome that our various internal organs help us both to adjust to the constant changes which occur in and around us and to navigate a steady course toward whatever we consider a worthwhile goal. Through the constant interplay between mind/body, man has the power to influence his adaptation. We cannot avoid stress, but we can control 'distress' and keep its damaging effects to a minimum," says Dr. Selye.

The secret to happiness lies in the successful adaptation to ever-changing conditions. Inability or unwillingness to adapt leads to disease and unhappiness. Effective adaptation can only occur if the pleasure of achievements far outweighs the pain of change. Many people refuse to adapt, change, or relearn. Thus any adaptation becomes more complicated and more difficult.

THE MANAGEMENT OF STRESS

We have defined stress. We have identified sources of stress inside and outside of the dental environment. We have briefly described personality characteristics that may affect a person's ability to cope with stressors. We have also detailed some of the effects of stress on the physical and mental well-being of individuals. How does a person control this inevitable force in the daily dental workplace? How does one turn a potentially negative influence into a productive, positive motivator?

The skill of stress management can be learned! Identifying a stressor and your own ability or inability to handle it is the first step in stress control. Awareness is the first step toward growth or change.

Let's identify some of the specific stressors that may be leading to your stress. Following are some of the things that cause the most stress in the work environment:

- Too much work
- Too little work
- Poor direction at work
- Poor organization or ineffective systems
- Workaholism
- Not being able to stay on top of technical advancements
- Special stresses
    - challenges for women in the workplace
    - single parents (dad or mom)
- Travel—catching up when one gets back home
- Inability to relax
- Substance abuse
- Poor communication

Take a few moments and do the following exercise. Since step one to stress control is to identify your stressors, please do yourself a favor, and take that step. Once you have identified the things causing stress for you, you can begin applying everything that I have taught you in this book to gain control of those stressors so they do not become "distress" points.

MY PERSONAL LIST OF STRESSORS

List those things that are stressors in your life. List them in order of intensity—1 being low intensity and 10 being high intensity. Then make a note as to whether or not you choose to take action to control each particular stressor (Fig. 14-1).

		I will work at reducing this stress	I will not work at reducing this stress
10.			
9.			
8.			
7.			
6.			
5.			
4.			
3.			
2.			
1.			

Fig. 14-1: List of Stressors and Approaches to Reducing Them

12 WAYS TO CONTROL STRESS AND ENERGIZE YOUR LIFE

12 steps to successful stress control

(1) **Focus on your vision.** Determine what you see as "ideal" in both your personal and professional life. Write this out in detail. Make sure your vision is clear and that when you ask the question "Will accomplishing this goal help us to reach our ultimate mission or fulfill our ultimate purpose?" that the answer is "yes".

(2) **Write your individual and team goals.** Together, focus on where you are, where you are going, and how you intend to get there.

A well-prepared person and/or team with a vision and specifically written goals has a focused direction. This will affect confidence and will make way for great accomplishment.

Set realistic goals. Positive thinking that is not supported by planned action is simply wishful thinking. Learn the art and science of goal setting (Chapter 2). Study and become motivated by the actual results that people are seeing in their lives and in their practices as a result of setting goals and disciplining themselves to bring those goals into realities. Realistic goals and appropriately related behavior lead to achievement.

Prioritize your goals. As was discussed in Chapter 2, prioritize your goals—high, medium, and low. Honor your prioritization. By prioritizing your goals, you will be able to see what is most important to you and your team. Your goals and the way they are prioritized should reflect your vision or purpose.

Prioritization will help you focus on the high priority areas of the practice—those areas/systems that will make a significant difference in the health and well being of the practice (*e.g.*, comprehensive treatment planning and thorough case presentation).

KEYPOINT:

Get your mind set. Confidence will lead you on.

—*Chinese proverb*

(3) Practice good time management. Practicing good time management is a must in today's busy world. In my opinion, one of the best time management strategies is to write and prioritize goals. Too many times, people complain they don't have time for really important things such as exercise, family, or good treatment plans. If you prioritize your days and your life, you will have time to do anything you really want to do.

Follow the time management strategy that I outlined in Chapter 2. Allow me to summarize here. At the end of every day, write down six things you need to do the next day. Prioritize those things. Then, put this list in a safe place where you can see it first thing the next day. The next day when you arrive at work, read your list. Start on your top priority item. Focus on it with intensity. Even though you will be interrupted numerous times, go back to your project when you can. Stay on that project until it is completed. Cross it off, and go to the next task, and so on.

You will find that your mind will relax because you have organized it. Otherwise, even when you are asleep, the subconscious mind, which never sleeps, will work frantically at trying to get your next day and all those "to dos" organized. You will wake up feeling like you haven't rested at all.

Read books, listen to tapes, or go to a course on time management. Honor your time. It is one of your most precious commodities.

(4) Exercise on a regular basis for physical and emotional well-being. Without question, one of the most effective ways to control stress is through regular exercise. Studies have proven that during exercise, tranquilizing chemicals called endorphins are released into the brain. This natural chemical brings about a pleasurable sensation.

Physicians who study the positive effects of exercise on the mind/body encourage a minimum of 30 minutes of vigorous exercise three to four times per week, with five times per week being even more effective. The key to the success of an exercise program is not how exhausted you can get, but to exercise your heart on a regular, cyclical basis.

Consider these exercise programs:

- Walking
- Swimming
- Jogging
- Bicycling
- Cross-country skiing

Warm up and stretch before beginning any exercise session. Don't overdo it. Increase the amount of exercise a little at a time. Cool down at the completion of each exercise session. In addition to stretching and cardio-vascular exercise, muscle-toning exercises are recommended. Not only will these exercises help maintain your strength and tone, but they will help you handle some of the challenging body positions you must maintain for long periods of time at the dental chair or at the computer. There are numerous benefits to strength training, one of which is to offset osteoporosis for both men and women.

Consider accessing the assistance of a professional to help you develop a program of exercise and fitness that is best for you. They may recommend a program that blends cardiovascular workouts with strength training and stretching.

Always consult your physician before embarking on an exercise program.

(5) **Practice proven relaxation techniques.** Invest in courses for employees on stress management. This will come back to the practice as a fabulous investment. There will be less sick leave and much greater productivity. Pay attention to prevention of stress-related problems. Don't fail to realize that the results of uncontrolled stress can be harmful. Incompetent management of human resources (team members) is one of the greatest wastes in the cost of doing business today.

People tend to blame stress for driving them to the brink of loss of control. They blame their jobs for this stress. This does not need to happen at all. Each person chooses how he or she will respond or adapt to the stresses that are a part of modern day dentistry. Take care of yourself as a good manager of your greatest gift and asset—You! Learn to relax!

Dr. Herbert Benson, in his well-known best seller, *The Relaxation Response*, states "the relaxation response is the inborn capacity of the body to enter a special state characterized by lowered heart rate, decreased rate of breathing, lowered blood pressure, slower brain waves and an overall reduction of the speed of metabolism. These changes produced by the relaxation response counteract the harmful effects and uncomfortable feelings of stress."

The following is a synopsis of Dr. Benson's relaxation response (Fig. 14-2). The results are phenomenal and have proven beneficial. The few moments spent in concentrated relaxation and control are worth the results and far outweigh the opposite—lost control!

Dr. Benson recommends that the relaxation response be practiced for 15-20 minutes two times per day, preferably morning and evening. Once

THE RELAXATION RESPONSE

1. Sit quietly in a comfortable position and loosen any tight clothing around your waist (if possible)
2. Close your eyes
3. Deeply relax all your muscles, starting with your feet and moving up to your head. Keep your muscles relaxed
4. Breathe in through your nose and out through your mouth. Become aware of your breathing. As you breathe out, repeat a word or brief phrase over and over in your mind such as "one." Breathe in, then out and think "one." Breathe in easily and naturally through your nose. Breathe into your stomach. Breathe out through your mouth. Sometimes your breaths will be deeper than others; that's okay. Continue.
5. Continue for 15–20 minutes. You may open your eyes to check the time, but do not use an alarm, or you will subconsciously prepare for the ringing of the alarm
6. When you finish, sit quietly for several minutes. Keep your eyes closed. Then after a minute or two, open them. Do not stand up immediately

Do not become distressed if your mind wanders. It will. Just recognize the thought and quietly bring your mind back to concentrating on the breathing and the repeating of your word or phrase. Once you have mastered the skill, you can gain control of yourself and your stress by practicing even for a few minutes when a brief break is available.

Fig. 14-2: The Relaxation Response

mastered, the technique can be performed at any time for even a few minutes with positive effects. Through the relaxation response, such physical changes as the following can be induced:

- Lowering of heart and breathing rates
- Lowering of blood pressure

- Improvement of the body's immune mechanisms
- Increased levels of killer "T" white blood cells in the bloodstream
- Elevation of circulating levels of endorphins (making pain tolerance greater)
- Control of headaches, even migraines

OTHER EFFECTIVE RELAXATION TECHNIQUES

Hobbies

Do something you really enjoy, and do it on a regular basis for at least one half-hour per day. These activities can provide a creative outlet totally different from the activities of your working day. In addition to hobbies such as sewing, reading, music, carpentry, gardening, cooking, and sports, look into adult education programs—civic and church activities. The change will reduce stress and fatigue while refreshing the creative part of your mind.

Meditation

Similar to the relaxation response, the various forms of meditation have proven effective in reducing stress through the power of the mind. These techniques are not necessarily tied to any specific religious belief.

Biofeedback

Special medical instruments handled by a skilled instructor can help a person control their reaction to specific situations. Again, the mind is trained to control the bodily responses.

Hypnosis

This technique can be used to bring about a relaxed, stress-free state in a person. It can also be used to break stress-related habits such as overeating, smoking, alcohol, and drug abuse.

Visualization

Taking an imaginary trip to a pleasant location, one from your past or a hoped-for trip of the future can relax the mind and the body. Close your eyes, take a deep breath, and for a brief 5 to 10 minutes, imagine the details of your dream location. Visualize the scene in detail. For example: feel the warm sun on your skin. Hear the waves crashing on the shore. See the environment.

In this brief trip, you can relax into a vacation-like state.

Massage

Give yourself permission to schedule regular massages into your life. These healthy sessions will relax the tension in your muscles and will release toxins that accumulate in your body. Certainly, I hope you practice excellent ergonomics in your practice, but no matter how correct your posture at the chair or the computer, your body will still experience stress. Massage will work wonders to relieve that stress.

Sleep

Get enough sleep. Seven hours per night are recommended for an adult.

(6) Feed your body properly. Eat properly. "You are what you eat!" Eat a balanced diet—carbohydrates, protein, and fat. Eat sensibly. Know that any eating plan based on extremes is probably robbing a part of your body of necessary nutrients. Read and study the principles of good eating. In addition, work with an expert in nutrition to evaluate a program of supplementation that would be healthy for you.

We raise registered quarter horses. These are high-powered show horses that are asked to perform excellently every day. We watch everything they eat and have an individualized program for each horse based on their requirements. We wouldn't put junk food into their bodies and then ask them to perform excellently. You are so much more valuable than any show horse in the world. Feed yourself every bit as carefully. Then, when you ask your body to function excellently, it will have been well fed and nourished and will be able to perform well. Everyone knows that nothing is more valuable than health, and yet we take it for granted. Be grateful for your health, and work at keeping it!

Don't kid yourself into thinking that you can eliminate or control stress with substance abuses. Make sure that you moderate or eliminate your intake of alcohol, caffeine, nicotine, and barbit-urates/tranquilizers. Control your stress naturally with a commitment to health of mind and body.

(7) Feed your mind positively. Feed your mind as carefully as you feed your body. It has been said that you will be the same person next year as you are this year except for the food you eat, the people you meet, and the books you read.

Your mind doesn't know the difference between reality and non-reality. When you feed negative stuff into your brain, it believes it. Be careful. Remember: "You become what you think about."

Listen to healthy, stimulating music. Watch healthy movies and TV. Read constructive, healthy books. Surround yourself with positive people. I never close my eyes at night without reading something positive, even if it is one sentence on those nights when I'm too tired to keep my eyes open. I want to put my mind to sleep on something positive. Rest will be sounder, and awakening will be more positive.

It's so easy to wallow in negative thoughts. You must make a conscientious effort to overpower the influence of negativity. Value yourself enough to make a decision to be positive. Look at the good things in your work, in your co-workers, and in yourself rather than looking for the bad. In his book, *The Power Of Positive Thinking*, Dr. Norman Vincent Peale says: "Things become better when you expect the best instead of the worst, for the reason that being freed from self-doubt, you can put your whole self into your endeavor, and nothing can stand in the way of a person who focuses his/her self on a

KEYPOINT:

Your mind doesn't know the difference between reality and non-reality. When you fed negative stuff into your brain, it believes it. Be careful. Remember: "You become what you think about."

KEYPOINT:

If you live your live expecting the best and nothing less, nothing can stand in your way.

problem." If you live your life expecting the best and nothing less, nothing can stand in your way.

(8) Stimulate your creative center by being innovative within your practice and with hobbies and outside activities. Create mental fitness in the workplace. Do this by continuing to learn the newest developments in your field, by adopting a positive approach, and by keeping the right side (the creative side) of the brain actively seeking and receiving creative solutions. Then you can actually reduce the number of bad days.

Outside of the office, ask yourself: "What do I really love to do? What gives me ultimate joy?" Make a list of things you personally love to do. Then, as you are organizing your time, schedule these things into your life. Stimulate the creative part of your being. Maximize your talent—all aspects of that talent. Talent that lies dormant will fester within and become like a raging tumor. It has to come out. Let it out in a constructive manner.

Schedule time for these activities. Otherwise, they will fall on the back burner.

(9) Communicate effectively; face stressful situations head on with constructive confrontation skills. Study and learn excellent communication skills (as taught in this book). Study skills that can be used to more effectively listen and speak. Access the skill and knowledge of confrontation so that conflicts can be resolved constructively. Communicate effectively with other team members, with patients, and with family.

(10) Organize every aspect, every system within your practice; pay attention to detail; do things right the first time; eliminate chaos; chaos breeds stress. Commit to getting and maintaining organization in all parts of your practice. Have excellent management systems in place and have talented, well-trained people engineering those systems. There are approximately 25 management systems in a dental practice. All 25 must be functioning excellently. They are so intricately connected that even if 24 systems are working well, but one system is off, that one will take away from the health and well-being of the other 24. Get a management coach in your life to analyze your practice and help you to get it "fit."

(11) Eliminate the things in your life that are not working and focus on and give attention to the things that are; get control of your life instead of letting your life control you; all of life is a matter of choice. The person who works at having a positive attitude and surrounds him/herself with positive people will always outshine the person who wallows in negativity, despair, and gloom. Be courageous enough to identify things that may have worked once upon a time, but are not working any more. If you identify a stressful place in your life, change or eliminate it.

In addition, care enough about yourself to refuse to let negativity drain the very life from you. If you are your own greatest source of negativity, learn to identify when you are becoming negative. Stop and imagine cutting that negative thought out of your brain. Fill the void with something positive—positive self-talk, a positive person who will support you, a positive reading (even if it's just a sentence or two), positive music, etc. Soon, you will not have any room for the negative. Your mind will be filled with the positive, and that is exactly what will come out.

Focus on and give attention to the things in your life that are working. The key to stress management is control. Learn to accept what you can't control, and learn to control what you can. All of life is a matter of choice. Remember: you are the manager of your own self. Choose healthily and wisely.

(12) Strive for and work toward achieving a balance in your life—a balance of love, work, worship, and play (Aristotle/L.D. Pankey). This is easier said than done. However, the positive results make your efforts worthwhile. If you feel out of sorts, depressed, listless—basically, out of balance—look carefully at these four areas of your life and make an honest evaluation. You will probably find that one or another of these four areas is lacking. Do whatever you need to do to fill the void.

You will probably never be in perfect balance. But I encourage you to be in a constant state of working toward that balance. Analyze where your imbalance lies. Reestablish that balance. Balance equals stress control.

IN SUMMARY

In summary, when dental professionals have been exposed to one or more stressors, there are two reactions that might take place:

- Psychological reaction
- Physiological reaction

Psychological reaction to stress has been found to increase a person's anxiety, has led to depression, and may cause decreasing job satisfaction. The behavioral consequences that occur as a result of this psychological reaction to stress may be:

- reduced job performance
- absenteeism
- tardiness
- job turnover
- interpersonal conflict

Physiological reaction to stress leads to such physical problems as:

- high blood pressure
- gastric problems
- headaches and migraines
- colds and flu
- difficulty sleeping

These two reactions to stressors—psychological and physiological—are interrelated in that psychological disorders, or a person's inadequate ability to cope with daily dental stresses, can cause or lead to physiological disease. On the other hand, physiologic reaction and disease will affect a person's productivity on the job, adding to absenteeism, tardiness, and job turnover.

Stressful situations in the dental environment will never be eliminated, but they can be controlled. Developing coping strategies and learning how to deal constructively with the daily activities of the dental profession and with daily living are essential if stressors are not to take a negative toll.

- Give those with whom you work your trust and confidence. Be patient and understanding. Be honest and committed
- Give those you love more of your time and focused attention
- Give yourself rest, proper nutrition, mental and physical exercise, relaxation, play, dreams, and goals
- Give yourself a lifetime of purpose by pursuing work that you love. If you retire, turn your energy to another type of work that fulfills a purpose
- Give yourself a sense of challenge each and every day
- Give yourself and the people with whom you interact the benefits of effective communication skills. Care enough to communicate

...And, in Conclusion...

If you have definitely determined what you want and have fixed a goal for yourself, then consider yourself extremely fortunate for you have taken the first step that will lead to your success. As long as you hold on to that mental picture of your idea and begin to develop it with action, nothing can stop you from succeeding. The subconscious mind never fails to obey any order given to it clearly and emphatically.

— CLAUDE BRISTOL

The first writing of this book was the accomplishment of an important goal for me. The book has been well received by the profession and has been on PennWell's bestseller list since its release. I am gratified to know that the information shared in the book has helped many dental professionals find greater joy and satisfaction in their practices.

Now, the second edition—another extremely important goal for me— has become a reality. The information is foundationally sound and effective. Seeing these concepts of great communication successfully integrated into more than 1,700 practices has made it clear that the strategies are workable and productive. The updating and expansion of the information are important. Changing and developing as the industry changes and develops are essential parts of my commitment to dentistry.

In addition, since the first edition, I have completed my doctorate, which has been a goal of my entire adult life. Having completed that major goal and having been able to validate the premises put forth in this book are benchmarks in my career and in my life. It is with pleasure that I integrate some of the doctoral study into this book so each and every one of you can have a more stress-controlled, productive, and enjoyable career and life.

COMMUNICATION AND RELATIONSHIPS

I remain convinced that communication is the bottom line to success in the dental practice, and in all of your relationships for that matter. Whether communicating with members of the team or with patients—personal, professional, and financial success is made or broken by the manner in which communication takes place. Perhaps, more importantly than any of this, how you communicate with your loved ones will certainly make a difference in your relationships. Please take all of the skills presented in this book home with you. Communication can make or break any relationship.

Becoming more attentive and accurate in your listening skills alerts you to the perceived needs of others. With this powerful information, you can be about the business of answering those needs. You expand your people skills and bond with your patients by developing a common thread of respect and mutuality.

By speaking and expressing yourself clearly and effectively, you can access results that you could not otherwise achieve. You will keep the lines of communication open. Closing the doors to communication will not get you where you want to go. Be ever aware of Paul Harvey's classic statement: "It's not what you say, it's how you say it!"

Conflicts *will* arise. Understanding the differences between people and knowing how to function with rather than against other people moves you forward. Otherwise, relationships go nowhere, or backwards. When conflicts do arise, you can now face them positively because you have the armamentarium to turn conflicting situations into caring relationships. Even though there will be times when you hurt each other's feelings, when communication lines seem to have been shut off, when the stress of the relationship seems irreparable, stop and listen. Listen to your heart. Ask yourself, "If we could work this out and be better on the other side of this conflict, would I want that?" If the answer to that very powerful question is "yes," then work on resolution. I always encourage people to identify the problem. Work diligently at solving the problem. Then, if the problem cannot be resolved, other measures may need to be taken. But don't throw in the towel too early. It's easier to walk away from a problem than it is to stand and face it. When you face it and use effective problemsolving skills, most any situation can be resolved if you want it to be resolved.

Most people don't like to confront because they are afraid of the repercussions. The main reason there are repercussions is that most people have not been taught effective communication skills, which include confrontation—confronting with care. You now know how to do just that—confront with care. However, if you use the listening and speaking skills and the constructive confrontation skills, you will be able to address problems while they are small and you will prevent most conflict.

What I have taught you in this book is preventive management. Makes sense to me!

KEYPOINT:

Spend more time on prevention so that you spend less time on cleaning up problematic situations.

COMMUNICATION AND PRODUCTION: THE RELATIONSHIP

With excellent communication skills that become the underlying foundation of successful case presentations, more people will say "yes" to your recommendations. Personal and professional fulfillment will result. You will be providing the type of dental care in which you believe and have spent a lifetime studying and perfecting. Rather than doing "patchwork" dentistry, you will be providing more comprehensive dental care. When the production increases, the profitability of the practice should increase as well. When the profits of the practice increase, it is my hope that all of you, every member of the team, will be able to share in the reward of work well done. There isn't a dental professional in the world that is paid too much. You are paid well. You make good salaries. But none of you are paid too much. You provide an amazing service to humanity. You help people to become comfortable, healthier, live longer lives, be more beautiful, and to have healthier self-images. Who provides a greater service?

Increasing your case acceptance through enhanced presentation skills benefits everyone. However, no matter how well you present your recommendations, there will be objections to face. Now you will be able to do so with a new attitude, an attitude that says, "Thanks for the objection. Now I know that you, Mrs. Patient, are interested in the proposal and are seeking answers to questions. If you didn't have those questions or those objections, you would be telling me that you are not interested. Not only will I look forward to your objections, but I will be able to handle them effectively."

Patients who become a part of your practice will not be walking out the door not receiving care. They will be walking out the door healthier, more beautiful, and happier than they were before they walked in. They will walk out happier, but they will come back because, as people professionals, you will have nurtured the relationship so they will not only come to you for treatment, but will stay with you for the duration. In addition, as happy, satisfied clients, they will refer other people to you that will receive the same, consistent care each and every time they enter your practice.

The six-step cycle of patient satisfaction that you want to accomplish is as follows:

- Through effective marketing, internal and external, people will come to you
- Through effective diagnosis, treatment planning, and case presentation, they will say, "yes" to treatment

- Through effective financing programs, they can willingly pay for the services
- Through effective scheduling, they will come to their appointments and will not cancel or not show up
- Through an effective hygiene program, they will stay with you for the long run
- Through effective referral systems, and because you are people professionals, they will refer to you

A COMMITMENT—THEN AND NOW

When Dr. Jim Saddoris of Tulsa, Oklahoma was the reigning President of the American Dental Association, he asked me to explain the process of my consultations with doctors and their teams. I showed him a graph outlining the 25 areas of the dental practice that we streamline when we go through a comprehensive consultation experience.

He asked, "Which of these 25 areas of concentration do doctors want and need the most, Cathy?"

Without hesitation, I answered, "Communication skills. This is usually the number one area of need and the number one area of requested help."

Therefore, we at Jameson Management, Inc., through our consulting/coaching, lectures, workshops, and writing, continue our commitment to teach communication skills and integrate those effective communication skills into every system within a practice—from scheduling to financing to case presentation and to all of the 25 management systems within a practice.

As a "forever student" myself, I will constantly be learning new and better ways to communicate. The day I stop learning is the day I need to stop teaching. This will never happen because I find that every opportunity I have to enhance my own communication skills enriches my relationships with family, friends, teammates, colleagues, and clients!

This is my hope for you, that by studying this book on communication skills, you will be richer personally, professionally, and financially. I truly know that if you will apply the skills held within this manuscript, you will grow and develop to a new level of confidence and, as a result, you will prosper in all areas of your life. I wish for you a life full of prosperity.

Call me with your successes. Call me when you realize that:

Great Communication Does Equal Great Production

GC=GP: A STUDY GUIDE

MEETING I — GOAL ACCOMPLISHMENT MEETING

Objective:

To understand the benefits of goal setting and to become proficient at the skill of writing goals and designing specific plans of action intended to bring goals to completion

Reading assignment:

Chapters 1 and 2—"Communication: The Bottom Line To Your Success" and "Goal Accomplishment"

Questions for discussion:

1. Define a goal.
2. What are the five reasons that 97% of all people do not write their goals? Discuss these reasons and how each applies to you and your team.

3. Write the five steps of goal accomplishment. Discuss the benefits of each, as well as how to do each.

Exercise:

1. Write one team goal. Write a complete action plan using the five-step process.

2. Under step 2, "Design a Plan of Action," identify necessary resources. Also, identify any barriers you may confront before reaching the goal. Determine how you will overcome that barrier.

Assignment:

1. Have each member of the team complete the form "This Year's Goals" from Chapter 2. Write at least three goals in each section— what the individual wants to accomplish in the practice this year, and what he/she would like to see the team accomplish.

2. Read these goals to each other at a team meeting. Then consolidate the team goals.

3. Prioritize those goals. Commit to a continuous review of those goals and to the implementation of the five-step process with each goal you want and intend to reach.

MEETINGS 2, 3, 4, 5, AND 6— BECOMING A PEOPLE PROFESSIONAL

Objective:

To develop the skills of customer/patient service that lead to patient satisfaction, loyalty, and referral. To become the epitome of people professionals committed to service above and beyond the expected.

Reading assignment:

Chapter 3—"Becoming a People Professional"

Additional Reading:

Raving Fans, Dr. Ken Blanchard
Fabled Service, Betsy Sanders

Questions for discussion:

1. Define "people professional" in your own terms. What does that mean to you and your team?
2. Review the ways to become a people professional
3. Separate the 10 areas into 5 meetings so you can thoroughly study and implement the strategies

   Meeting 2 = 1
   Meeting 3 = 2
   Meeting 4 = 3
   Meeting 5 = 4 – 6
   Meeting 6 = 7 – 10

MEETING 2—(AREA 1)

Exercise and assignment:

1. Write or review and refine your own mission statement. Discuss that statement:
   - Does it describe who you are and what you do, and is it empowered by strong, emotional words and phrases?
   - Does the statement send a clear message of your values? What are those values?

MEETING 3—(AREA 2)

Exercise and assignment:

1. Review Area 2

2. Write a patient survey to determine what services are desired by your patients. What do they like most about your practice? What would they like to see improved?

3. Give or send those questionnaires out to patients. Then schedule time to discuss the results.

4. Use the information to improve.

MEETING 4—(AREA 3)

Exercise and assignment:

1. Review Area 3.

2. Review all phases of a patient's experience with you, from the initial telephone call through the final treatment.

3. Discuss each step and determine ways you can apply exquisite etiquette to each. What kinds of "special things" can you do to make a patient's experience with you extra special?

4. Read Chapter 9—"Communication via The Telephone" and review all.

MEETING 5—(AREAS 4 - 6)

Exercise and assignment:

1. Review Areas 4-6.

2. Area 4: Discuss your service mix. Determine (questionnaire feedback will help) what services your patients are particularly interested in receiving. How can you offer more of those services?

Determine the following:

- Necessary reading material
- Courses to attend
- Marketing strategies

Order and review *Collect What You Produce* from PennWell Corporation (800-752-9764). Discuss the financial services discussed in this book. Order and listen to Jameson Management tapes on financing. Role play the verbal skills of presenting financial options and overcoming objections.

3. Area 5: Go over all notes of case presentation as recommended by Cathy in Chapter 10. Discuss each step and role-play. Discuss how you can become better educators. Who will do what, when, and how? Practice, practice, practice.

4. Area 6: Review the types of treatment you are providing, the benefits of going ahead with such treatment and the risks involved if the patient does not proceed with recommended treatment. Make sure that both the clinical and business teams are "in sync" with their communication/verbal skills. The consistency of education and of back-up support is critical.

MEETING 6—(AREAS 7 - 10)

Exercise and assignment:

1. Review Areas 7, 8, 9, and 10.

2. Area 7: Practice getting great before and after photographs of all patients who receive treatment. Determine how you will log this data for review. In addition, make sure that you look at and discuss the results of treatment with each patient.

3. Area 8: Discuss how you will handle difficult cases or situations in which things don't go as well as would be desired. Make sure all team members are clear on policy and role-play how such discussions need to go.

4. Area 9: Discuss ways you can stay in constant contact with your patients. Come to a consensus agreement on four plans of actions— four contacts over the next year. Stay in touch with your patient family every three months (good practice building).

5. Area 10: Review these data and all decisions made once per month to make sure you are on course or to see if the plan of action needs

to be adjusted. Review, review, review. Constantly evaluate. That's teamwork. That's being a people professional.

Meeting 7 — Understanding Personality Differences

Objective:

To learn more about personality styles and how each of you can relate more effectively with each other and with patients by having a clear understanding of those differences.

Reading assignment:

Chapter 4—"Understanding Personality Differences"

Questions for discussion:

1. Discuss the four personality styles—the characteristics, the strengths, the differences.
2. Determine how you can identify the style of a patient.

Exercise and assignment:

1. Discuss how you can effectively meet the needs of different people by altering your presentation methodology.
2. Identify one patient per style in your practice.
3. Role-play a treatment presentation altering to fit each unique patient.

Additional reading:

Personality Styles, Florence Littauer

MEETING 8—LISTENING SKILLS

Objective:

To study and implement better listening skills so that patient's needs will become clearer and patients will know they are valued and respected. In addition, through better listening, case presentation will be enhanced, a higher rate of treatment acceptance will result, and productivity will rise.

Reading assignment:

Chapter 5—"Listen Your Way to Success: Refining the Art and Science of Listening"

Questions for discussion:

1. What is listening? Why is it considered the most valuable of all communication skills?
2. Describe the following, and discuss in detail:
   - body language
   - tone of voice
   - passive listening
   - active listening
3. What is getting in the way of you being a good listener? Does that have an impact on patients? How?

Exercise and assignment:

1. Identify the things that get in the way of you being a good listener. Discuss ways to eliminate or reduce those barriers.
2. Identify situations where you would like to do a better job of listening. What do you need to do to make that happen?
3. Work in groups of two. Each of you write down a problem that you are having at the present time. It doesn't have to be a major problem or concern. Discuss your concern with your partner. When you are the one listening, make sure that you practice all four of the listening skills. Do this for two or three minutes, then switch. The person who has been listening now shares her problem with the partner, and the other person becomes the listener. Do this for two or three minutes.

Now, give each other some constructive feedback on how your partner listened. Listening is tough! It takes practice.

MEETING 9—SPEAKING

Objective:

To learn to speak in a manner that gets and keeps doors of communication open. Also, become proficient in delivering "I" messages. (The first step of effective confrontation).

Reading assignment:

Chapter 6—"Getting Your Message Across in a Positive Way: Speaking Skills"

Questions for discussion:

1. Discuss the three goals of good speaking skills.
2. Discuss the flow of communication.

Exercise and assignment:

1. Review the seven steps of effective speaking.
2. Give examples of each step as they relate to patient communication.
3. Review the parts of an "I" message. Discuss the times when such a message is appropriate.
4. Identify a situation in your practice in which a patient's behavior was non-acceptable. Design an "I" message. Practice sending it to each other. Discuss.

Additional reading:

Leader Effectiveness Training, Dr. Thomas Gordon

Meeting 10—Confrontation

Objective:

To learn effective skills for handling difficult patients and difficult situations. To understand the benefits of positive confrontation and how to confront with care.

Reading assignment:

Chapter 7—"Handling Difficult People and Difficult Situations"

Questions for review:

1. Discuss the two main differences that may lead to conflict.
2. How does listening diffuse anger? How can listening become an asset in conflict resolution?
3. Describe the following:
    – positive disagreement
    – constructive confrontation
    – either/or confrontation

Exercise and assignment:

1. Identify examples of times when each of the three types of confrontation would be appropriate and beneficial. Create and deliver these types of confrontation in a role-play.
2. Discuss "the mirror effect."
3. Write down your personal intentions about developing and maintaining a positive attitude.

Meeting 11—Special People/Special Needs

Objective:

To discover effective ways to meet the needs of special people who have special needs and where special treatment is appropriate.

Reading Assignment:

Chapter 8—"Special People/Special Needs"

Questions for review:

1. How can you set up the environment to handle your children patients better?
2. How can you set up the environment to handle your geriatric patients better?

Exercise and assignment:

1. Write out positive words to use with children, and write out negative words that you want to eliminate.
2. Order children-friendly visual aids that will help children understand what is going on and will help them to feel more comfortable in your practice.
3. Contact the nursing homes in which some of your geriatric patients live. Discuss a program in which you can benefit these folks. Also, find out how you can be more accommodating when they bring a resident to your practice.

MEETING 12—COMMUNICATION VIA TELEPHONE

Objective:

To learn how to speak and listen effectively on the telephone, track incoming and outgoing calls, and handle difficult calls.

Reading assignment:

Chapter 9—"Communication via The Telephone"

Questions for review:

1. What are the four "musts" when making a phone call?
2. What are the four stages of an effective telephone call?
3. How can an irate caller best be handled?

Exercise and assignment:

1. Determine how all team members should answer the telephone and role play those skills.

2. Determine what tools to use for taking messages and gathering patient information. Fill out samples to have the team refer to if questions arise.

3. Determine how to track phone calls that are made to patients and follow that protocol.

4. Determine reasons why patients may call in to your practice being upset. Role-play the best ways to handle those phone calls.

MEETING 13—CASE PRESENTATION

Objective:

To learn and refine the skills of presenting treatment recommendations so that the majority of your patients choose to proceed. Learn to identify and overcome objections, so solutions to problems can be determined.

Reading assignment:

Chapters 10 and 11—"Making an Effective Case Presentation: Gaining Treatment Acceptance" and "Handling Objections."

Questions for discussion:

1. What goals are accomplished with an excellent protocol of case presentation?

2. What skills are valuable during case presentation? Describe and tell why.

3. What are the four main objections to treatment acceptance?

4. What are the six main motivators for dental treatment?

Exercise and assignment:

1. Define the six steps of the case presentation process. Detail each aspect of each step.

2. Role-play the initial interview.

3. Decide if you want to send a welcome packet. If so, what will go with each packet?

4. Discuss patient brochures and how to use them as an educational piece. Decide what types of brochures you need, who will order them, how you will use them, etc.

5. Practice asking closing questions to identify any objections or to ask for a commitment.

6. Name three key principles that are the foundation for identifying objections

7. List and discuss all seven steps of handling objections.

8. Name the four major objections to dental acceptance. Discuss ways to effectively overcome each of those objections. What solutions can you make possible in your practice? Together, decide how you will implement these solutions. When you determine ways to handle these four major objections, you will take the lid off your practice.

MEETING 14—FINANCIAL COMMUNICATION

Objective:

To learn how to discuss the financial aspects of treatment to overcome one of the major barriers to treatment acceptance—cost.

Reading assignment:

Chapter 12—"Financial Communication: The Final Close"

Questions for discussion:

1. What are the major objections you hear when patients speak of fees?

2. Discuss your financial options. Do you have all the options discussed in Chapter 12? If not, which ones would be of benefit to you and your patients?

Exercise and assignment:

1. Call healthcare financing companies. Get and study their data. Determine which programs would be best for you, and get involved.
2. Practice the verbal skills of handling questions about cost, objections about your fees, and questions about how a patient can pay for their dental care.
3. Brainstorm ways to introduce a healthcare financing program into your practice. Using the five-step goal accomplishment process, design plans of action for integrating these programs into your practice so more people will be able to proceed with treatment.

Additional reading:

Collect What You Produce, Cathy Jameson, Ph.D.

MEETING 15—REFERRALS

Objectives:

To build the practice from within by developing a healthy new patient flow from existing patient referrals.

Reading assignment:

Chapter 13—"Nurture Personal Referrals: Your Best Source of New Patients"

Questions for discussion:

1. Why do people refer to you? Be specific.
2. Are you nurturing referrals presently? How? In what ways?

Exercise and assignment:

1. Role-play asking for referrals.
2. Identify patients each day that need to be invited to refer. Who will ask? How? When?

3. How can you give incentive and reward referrals? Determine three specific ways, and implement the plan.

4. Develop a practice internal marketing strategy that will nurture increased referrals.

MEETING 16—STRESS CONTROL

Objective:

To learn about positive and negative stress. To identify stressors. To learn strategies for controlling stress. The goal is a more relaxed, comfortable, and fun dental environment.

Reading assignment:

Chapter 14—"Controlling Stress in the Dental Profession Through Effective Communication: A Doctoral Dissertation"

Questions for discussion:

1. Define positive and negative stress.

2. Describe stressors in your practice.

3. What are negative effects of uncontrolled stress?

Exercise and assignment:

1. Complete the exercise on identifying stressors and prioritizing the intensity of those stressors. Discuss what you will do about each of them.

2. Study and practice the relaxation response.

3. Study the 12 ways to control stress and energize your life. Write out what you are going to do to apply each of these 12 ways to your life.

Additional reading:

The Relaxation Response, Herbert Benson, M.D.
Stress for Success, Peter Hanson, M.D.

Adams, Linda. *Be Your Best.* New York: The Putnam Publishing Group, 1989

Adler, Mortimer. *How to Speak, How to Listen.* New York: Macmillan Publishing Co., 1983

Ash, Mary Kay. *On People Management.* New York: Harper and Row, 1984

Benson, M.D., Herbert. *The Relaxation Response.* New York: Morrow and Co., 1975

Blanchard, Ph.D., Kenneth, and Spencer Johnson, M.D. *The One-Minute Manager.* New York: Berkeley Books, 1982

Blanchard, Kenneth. *Raving Fans.* New York: William Morrow and Co., Inc., 1993

Caplan, D.D.S., Carl. *Dental Practice Management Encyclopedia.* Tulsa, OK: PennWell Books, 1985

Carkhuff, R.R. *Helping and Human Relations: A Primer for Lay and Profession Helpers*

Christen, A.G. "Stress and Distress in Dental Practice," *Occupational Hazards in Dentistry.* Chicago: Yearbook Medical Publishers, Inc., 1984

Cinotti, D.D.S., William, Arthur Grieder, D.D.S., and Robert Heckel, Ph.D. *Applied Psychology in Dentistry.* St. Louis: C.V. Mosby, 1964

Couture, Ph.D., Gary. *The Quantum Breakthrough in Communication.* Newport Beach, CA: Institute for Advanced Educational Research

Covey, Stephen R. *Principle-Centered Leadership.* New York: Simon & Schuster, Inc., 1991

Dahl, Dan, and Randolph Sykes. *Charting your Goals.* New York: Harper and Row, 1983

Daley, M. *Burnout. Smoldering Problem in Protective Services.* Social Work, 24, 375, September 1979

Dworkin, D.D.S., Samual, Thomas Ferrence, Ph.D., and Donald Gidden, Ph.D. *Behavioral Science and Dental Practice,* St. Louis: C.V. Mosby, 1978

Eliot, M.D., Robert. *From Stress To Strength.* New York: Bantam Books, 1994

Folger, Joseph and Poole Marshall. *Working Through Conflict,* Glenview, IL: Scott, Foresman, 1982

Foreman, Ed. *Happy, Healthy, and Terrific.* Dallas: Executive Development Systems, 1988

Foreman, Ed. *Laughing, Loving, and Living.* Dallas: Executive Development Systems, 1982

Gordon, Thomas. *Leader Effectiveness Training.* New York: Peter Wyden Publishers, 1977

Gordon, Thomas. *Parent Effectiveness Training.* New York: Peter Wyden Publishers, 1974

Hanson, M.D., Peter G. *The Joy of Stress.* Canada: Hanson Stress Management Organization, Inc., 1985

Hanson, M.D., Peter G. *Stress for Success.* Canada: Hanson Stress Management Organization, Inc., 1989

Hendrix, Ph.D., William. "Dental Stress and Assessment Questionnaire." Dental Clinics of North America. Philadelphia: W.B. Saunders, October 1986

Hopkins, Tom. *How to Master the Art of Selling.* Scottsdale, AZ: Warner Books, 1982

Hopkins, Tom. *The Official Guide to Success.* Arizona: Tom Hopkins International, Inc., 1982

Jackson, Eric. "Stress Management and Personal Satisfaction in Dental Practice." Dental Clinics of North America. Philadelphia: W.B. Saunders, 1977

Kanner, A., D. Kafry, & Pines. *Conspicuous in its Absence: The Lack of Positive Conditions as a Source of Stress.* Journal of Human Stress, 4, December 1978

Karrass, Gary. *Negotiate to Close.* New York: Simon & Schuster, Inc., 1985

Katz, D.D.S., Clifford. "Stress Factors Operating in the Dental Office Work Environment." Dental Clinics of North America. Philadelphia: W.B. Saunders, October 1986, pp S29-S36

LaHaye, Tim. *Spirit-Controlled Temperament.* California: Post, Inc., 1966

LeBoeuf, Michael. *The Greatest Management Principle.* Chicago: Nightingale-Conant, 1986

Littauer, Florence. "How to Understand Others by Understanding Yourself." Personality Plus. New Jersey: Power Books, 1983

Maslach, C. *Burn Out.* Human Behavior 5, 16, September 1976

Miller, Ph.D., Lyle, and Alma Dell Smith, Ph.D. *The Stress Solution.* New York: Pocket Books, 1993

Nevin, Ph.D., Robert, and Vicki Sampson, M.S. *Dental Family Stress and Coping Patterns.* Dental Clinics of North America. Philadelphia: W.B. Saunders, October 1986, pp. 117-131

Peale, Dr Norman Vincent, *The Power of Positive Thinking.* New York: Fawcett Crest, 1952.

Pillow, William. *Communication with Patients.* Indianapolis: Eli Lilly and Co., 1985

Selye, M.D., Hans. *Stress Without Distress.* New York: Signet, 1974

Selye, M.D., Hans. *The Stress of Life.* New York: McGraw-Hill, 1978

Solomon, Muriel. *Working With Difficult People.* New Jersey: Prentice Hall, 1990

Swogger, M.D., Glenn. "The Type A Personality, Overwork, and Career Burnout." Dental Clinics of North America. Philadelphia: W.B. Saunders, October 1986, pp. 37–44

Verderber, Rudolph. *Communicate.* Belmont, CA: Wadsworth Publishing Company, 1987

Willingham, Ron. *The Best Seller—The New Psychology of Selling and Persuading People.* Englewood Cliffs. New Jersey: Prentice-Hall, 1984

Ziglar, Zig. *Ziglar On Selling.* Nashville, TN: Oliver-Nelson Books, 1991

Ziglar, Zig. *See You At The Top.* Gretna: Pelican Publishers, 1988

INDEX

Q

W

Y

JAMESON MANAGEMENT, INC.
THE COMPANY'S MISSION AND VISION

The mission of Jameson Management, Inc. is to serve the health-care industry as a consulting and lecturing service that provides both business and personnel management. The following is a statement of mission and purpose for Dr. Cathy Jameson and Jameson Management, Inc. consulting services:

1. To make a positive difference in the lives of the professionals whom we have the privilege to serve.
2. To teach practice management with a heart.
3. To teach practical skills of business and personnel management.
4. To facilitate excellent relationships between and among team members via the teaching of effective communication skills.
5. To help team members understand these communication skills and be able to serve patients better because of productive communication.
6. To integrate business systems that will lead the way to productivity and profitability for the practitioners and the entire team.
7. To teach systems that are time efficient, cost efficient, and will control stress.

CATHY JAMESON, Ph.D.

Dr. Cathy Jameson, and her team, conduct in-office consulting and continuing education seminars internationally. Thousands of dental professionals have benefitted from her programs focused on increasing productivity, profitability and controlling stress. Services offered by Jameson Management, Inc. include:

- In-office Business Management Consulting
- Technology Consulting
- Continuing Education Seminars
- Communication Skills Training
- Motivational Programs
- Leadership Training
- Team Building
- Power Symposiums/Specialized Training
- Supportive Products

For information on how Jameson Management can increase your practice's productivity, profitability and control stress, please contact:

Jameson Management, Inc.
P.O. Box 488
Davis, Oklahoma
Phone: 580- 369-5555
Fax 580-369-3352
Email: jameson@brightok.net
www.jamesonmanagement.com

IMPROVE YOUR PRACTICE WITH DR. CATHY JAMESON

COLLECT WHAT YOU PRODUCE

by Dr. Cathy Jameson   ($44.95, U.S.A.)

This book will help you define financial strategies appropriate to your practice and determine the skills needed to implement fiscally responsible collection practices. This guide includes scripts and letters ready for immediate use by your dental office team covering all aspects of financing. Take advantage of this exciting and informative guide today!

GREAT COMMUNICATION=GREAT PRODUCTION TAPES

by Dr. Cathy Jameson   ($29.95, U.S.A.)

This two cassette series is a perfect addition to your team meetings. You will be inspried by Cathy's non-stop energy in this easy to listen, power-packed series that gives you the information you need to improve communication in your practice, with your patients and with your team, in a quick study format.

SCHEDULE FOR PRODUCTIVITY, PROFITABILITY & STRESS CONTROL

by Dr. Cathy Jameson   ($149.00, U.S.A.)

An exciting, five tape series recorded before a live audience, this tape will teach you how to control each day with effective scheduling so that your days do not control you. With entertaining and educational insights, Cathy focuses on the scheduling strategies that involve the entire team.

EFFECTIVE COMMUNICATION: THE KEY TO CONTROLLING STRESS IN YOUR DENTAL PRACTICE

By Dr. Cathy Jameson ($197.00, U.S.A.)

In these two one-hour video sessions, you can learn the same skills and techniques over 1,700 dental practices have successfully implemented into their personal and professional lives. These videos are designed to reduce both the burnout and dropout of dental practice team members, improve job satisfaction, build stronger team and patient relationships, reduce the stress caused by team dysfunction or conflict, teach you how to handle difficult people and difficult situations, and increase office productivity through great communication.

THE DENTAL TEAM'S GUIDE TO PRODUCTIVE AND PROFITABLE DAYS

by Dr. Cathy Jameson ($89.00, U.S.A.)

This dynamic video outlines systems designed to make everyday great in your dental practice. Not only does this presentation tell you about the systems, it shows you how to perform them. Watch and learn how to conduct morning meetings, the 3-5 minute checkout (or patient transfer), the new patient experience, the consultation and financial arrangements. This is a powerful learning tool for the entire team!

Would you like more information on Jameson Management's services? To secure a free copy of a Jameson Management brochure, please complete the following form by PRINTING the information requested, and return the form to:

Jameson Management, Inc.
Attn: Practice Development Coordinator
P.O. Box 488
Davis, OK 73030

Or call:

Jameson Management, Inc.
580-369-5555
Fax: 580-369-3352
Email: Jameson@brightok.net

Yes, I have read *Great Communication = Great Production*, and I would like a complimentary brochure on Jameson Management's services and products.

My name is

_____

My practice name is

_____

My business address is:

_____

_____

City _____ State _____ Zip _____

My business phone is:

_____

My home phone is:

_____

My business is:

†general practice _____

†specialty:_____

I have been in practice for:

_____

My key challenges are:

1._____

2._____

3._____

Please have a representative call me to discuss my practice.

I prefer to be called

(1) at work (phone): _____

(2) at home (phone): _____